African Apes

Also by B. F. BEEBE:

American Bears
American Desert Animals
American Lions and Cats
American Wild Horses
American Wolves, Coyotes and Foxes
Appalachian Elk
Assateague Deer
Chestnut Cub
Coyote Come Home
Ocelot
Run, Light Buck, Run
Yucatan Monkey
Animals South of the Border
African Elephants
African Lions and Cats

AFRICAN APES

by

B. F. Beebe

Illustrated by James Ralph Johnson

Johnson, Burdetta Faye

DAVID McKAY COMPANY, INC.   New York

AFRICAN APES

LIBRARY OF CONGRESS CATALOG CARD NUMBER: 76–81893
MANUFACTURED IN THE UNITED STATES OF AMERICA

To Mrs. Beulah Beebe,
Cherryvale, Kansas

Contents

African Apes

1: *Man's Distant Kin*

Perhaps the most man-like of chimpanzees in modern times was an adult male called Chumley. "You regarded him," said Gerald Durrell in his book *The Overloaded Ark*, "more as a fascinating, mischievous, courtly old man, who had for some reason best known to himself disguised himself as a chimpanzee. His manners were perfect . . ."

Chumley had been reared almost as a son by a government official in West Africa and Durrell first met the chimp after he had agreed to take him to the London Zoo where he could be properly cared for. He was too big for the official to maintain adequately.

Chumley arrived at Durrell's camp in a crate carried on a truck bed. When the crate was opened, Chumley stepped out with the self confidence of a film star. He looked about casually, then stuck out a hand to be shaken. This done he pulled his fifteen-foot chain—fastened around his neck—from the crate, looped it over one arm and walked into Durrell's hut. The surprised Durrell realized that the chimp had moved in and he remembered that he felt like apologizing to this cool, confident ape for the dirty dishes left on the table.

Chumley sat down and dropped the chain on the floor. Durrell realized then that the chimp expected some sort of refreshment after the trip. Shouting to a helper for tea, Durrell turned back to Chumley who had crossed his legs and was giving the hut a careful inspection. Durrell took out a cigarette pack, fished out a cigarette—and found a chimpanzee hand waiting a few inches away.

Wondering what would happen next, Durrell handed him a cigarette. Chumley calmly put it between his lips. Amazed at this, Durrell decided to see what he would do about lighting it. He handed the chimp a match box. Chumley opened the box, selected a match, struck it and lighted his cigarette. Then he leaned back in his chair, recrossed his legs and blew clouds of smoke into the air.

Shortly, when Chumley's tea was poured and sugar and milk added, the chimp grunted softly in satisfaction. Picking up the tea mug Chumley found the cigarette was too much to hold. He set the mug down, placed the cigarette on the table and lifted the mug again. To test the heat he stuck out a lip and sampled the tea. It was too hot, so he blew on it until it cooled sufficiently, then drank it, upending the mug to await the sliding melted sugar. Successful at last in gaining the last particle of sweetness he held out the mug for more tea.

Like so many chimpanzees Chumley loved to ride in a vehicle. When the time came for the move to England, the first stage was by truck from camp to ship. As animal crates and cages were loaded, Chumley showed his excitement with much hooting and jumping. As soon as Chumley's crate was lifted onto a truck he jumped aboard and climbed inside, anxious to get underway. As soon as the truck began moving the native staff members on the truck began singing. This was a delight to Chumley and he joined the chorus with "a prolonged and melodious hooting," as Durrell explained. The result sent the natives into such a fit of laughter that one fell off the truck.

The London Zoo's representative met the animal contingent on the coast and escorted them back to England. Four months later when the delayed Durrell arrived at the London Zoo he wondered if his old friend Chumley would remember him. He doubted it since he had a luxurious beard when he knew Chumley in Africa but was now clean shaven.

When Durrell was admitted to the large straw-filled room where Chumley lived at the zoo the chimpanzee whirled immediately and rushed happily to Durrell, biting his fingers gently in greeting.

The two sat down in the straw and enjoyed a smoke together while Chumley removed Durrell's shoes and socks. Then he examined the man's feet carefully to insure they were in good shape.

When Chumley's cigarette was finished he arose and walked to the corner of the room which was free of straw. Here he ground out his cigarette on the concrete floor. When Durrell arose to leave, Chumley shook hands solemnly and watched through the door crack until it was closed.

Chumley's enthusiasm for riding in vehicles was his

undoing. He escaped from his zoo enclosure twice, and loped across a park to the streets. On his first escape he swung aboard a bus at a stop and panicked passengers. Their outcries so unnerved him that he bit one. His second break-out was on Christmas Eve. There was no bus at the stop so he walked along a line of cars beating on their sides in his attempt to get someone to open a door and give him a ride. Frightened occupants, however, rolled up windows and screamed for help. Zoo personnel soon recaptured the disappointed ape who had tried so hard to integrate himself into man's world.

Chimpanzees with their bouncy extroverted personalities remind man more of a tenuous kinship than any of the world's other three apes. Like the races and cultures of man, the various apes have sharply diverging personalities and characteristics. Africa's chimpanzees and gorillas spend most of their time on the ground and live in much larger groups than Asian apes, gibbons and orangutans. The latter are primarily tree-dwellers, arboreal, and oddly the tailless gibbon is a better acrobat than any of the monkeys with tails which are always helpful as balancing poles and sometimes as fifth hands as in prehensile-tailed new world monkeys.

What is the difference between an ape and monkey? The most apparent is the fact that none of the apes have tails. Apes can swing hand over hand, or brachiate, with ease. Monkeys cannot do this nearly as well, not even the long-limbed spider monkey. The monkey has shoulder sockets facing down which limit true brachiation.

GIBBON ORANG—UTAN

GORILLA CHIMPANZEE

Strangely, man can brachiate better than monkeys if he is physically fit.

Ape arms have almost unbelievable strength and those animal collectors who have had the most experience with wild apes have the greatest respect for this strength. They consider an adult chimp as strong as three large men. One naturalist saw a native's face which had been laid open and scarred severely by a chimp that took a swipe at him. The owner of a chimpanzee reared in a home under similar circumstances as a child found that the pet at the age of five had no trouble swinging from a limb when suspended by only one finger.

Apes exhibit a surprising ability to balance while falling. A zoologist watched a chimpanzee fall seventy feet after a limb broke beneath it. It did not tumble but spread-eagled with legs and arms held slightly downward, a posture insuring balance and maximum opportunity to grab a limb on the way down. The chimp contacted no limbs, however, and landed heavily in the vegetation. The man tried to find the chimpanzee but could discover no trace. Apparently it was not hurt.

Monkeys are essentially four-footed, or quadrupeds. The pelvis is designed for this stance and they have no trouble walking with palms down although arms are shorter than legs. Ape arms are considerably longer than legs, yet apes place knuckles against the ground. Their arm and hand structures make the palms-down posture too uncomfortable. Monkey spines are relatively flexible. Ape spines are relatively inflexible. Surprisingly, man's spine is more flexible than the gorilla's.

Although monkeys and apes can stand erect briefly, neither can do so for long. Legs cannot be locked as can man's, nor are their hip muscles as large proportionately as man's buttocks which move man's body forward and over the leg during walking.

There are twenty-seven forms of living apes belonging to ten species. They fall into two stages—lesser and greater apes. The lesser apes include gibbons, concolors and siamangs. The great apes include the orangs, chimpanzees and gorillas. Only the last two are found in Africa.

The great apes share these distinguishing characteristics: plentiful, long, straight hair, short legs, long bodies and noneverted—essentially no—lips. Of the four races of man—Australoid, Caucasoid, Mongoloid and Negroid —the Negroid least resembles ape characteristics. The "white" man, Caucasoid, has features closest to those of the chimpanzee and gorilla. These resemblances, or lack of them, are meaningless since all races of man stand equidistant from the apes. Variations in man's physical differences, including colors, are nothing more than results of genetic variations of adaptations to environments.

Of all the primates, the great apes are closest to man in their development. Zoologists continue to be astounded at new discoveries which show that such activities as tool-making and tool-using, once thought exclusive to man, are shared by the chimpanzees. The large-brained gorilla has little use for tools because of its rich habitat which affords more than enough food the year round.

The two African apes differ sharply in personalities. The gorilla is the quiet aristocrat, confident in its ability to take care of itself. The chimpanzee is the noisy extrovert, easily excited and alarmed. Few primates, including man, demonstrate the grasp of leadership shown by a dominant male gorilla.

Gorilla groups are fairly stable and contain a dozen to three dozen individuals. They tend to remain within an area of about fifteen square miles. Chimpanzees use twice as large a home range and live in groups which change size constantly. Large chimpanzee groups contain about thirty individuals. Both species build nests, chimps almost entirely in trees and gorillas both in trees and on the ground.

Do chimpanzees and gorillas ever mate and produce hybrid offspring? Apparently they do not. Many reports from natives and other observers indicate that hybrids do exist, yet no examination of hundreds of chimpanzee skulls has shown an intermediate character between the two which would indicate crossbreeding.

Apparently gorillas and chimpanzees get along well together. In parts of western Uganda and eastern Congo where the species use the same territory there have been no observations of any contact between the two that was not peaceful.

Both species have vocabularies of similar size; the gorilla, twenty-two indentifiable sounds, the chimp, twenty-three. The chimpanzee's many facial expressions seem to enlarge the area of communication between individuals. The meaning of some of these, such as an exaggerated grin which means a threat, is not readily apparent to the human observer.

Gorillas show few emotional outbursts like chimpanzees who "whoop it up" at appropriate moments. Chimps meeting each other often throw arms around each other, smack their lips and jump up and down. Mothers of both species show patient devotion toward their infants.

Gorilla babies become independent earlier and stop riding their mothers' backs at about eighteen months while chimp babies ride their mothers as long as three years. Juveniles of both species play frequently with companions until about six.

At no time in the world's history has man been so interested in the ape and the monkey kingdom. Suddenly man has come to realize that many of the reasons why he behaves as he does might be answered by chimpanzees and gorillas and their kin in the monkey kingdom.

In the 1930's, Robert Yerkes saw the culmination of a dream he had nurtured since his Harvard days: an ape institution of higher learning, so to speak, where man could study ape psychology and its relationship to man. This was the Orange Park Research Station for Primate Studies in northeast Florida. In the years since, studies have generated more studies and a wealth of invaluable data has been accumulated.

Investigations of the ape have been underway also in other countries for many years. German scientist Wolfgang Kohler established an ape research colony in the Canary Islands in 1912. A collection of pet apes and monkeys assembled by Rosalia Abreu in Cuba during the 1920's was large enough to allow scientists like Yerkes valuable subjects with which to begin his early studies.

In 1913 a Russian woman, Nadie Kotts, began a study of a young chimpanzee reared in her home, and eighteen years later an Indiana couple, psychologist W. N. Kellogg and his wife, made independent studies of the same situation. These were only a few of the ape studies of importance begun in the first half of this century.

In 1948 Japan established the world's first primate research center to develop the science of primatology, the study of apes and monkeys. Since then seven primate centers have been established by the American government.

A tragic circumstance affecting a vast but unestimated number of parents of all human races is the fact that they are not psychologically adequate to the job of normal parenthood. Police departments of all large cities are painfully aware of cruelties inflicted on infant children by mothers or fathers whose tolerance of their offspring is subnormal. Apes and monkeys can be subject to the same tragedies.

Harry Harlow and his staff at the University of Wisconsin studied extensively the behavior of rhesus monkeys deprived of vital emotional securities during early life. Some had "mothers" constructed of cloth. Others had "mothers" of wire cylinders. Some monkey infants were kept in isolation and prevented from playing with other young monkeys. Consequently, Harlow found that the normal infant-infant relationship of early playmates usually erased the disadvantages of a lifeless substitute parent. Most male infant monkeys allowed adequate play with other infant monkeys during their first six months grew into normal adulthood. However, only one female denied these infant-infant relationships grew into normal adulthood.

Harlow mated some of these abnormal female adults to see how they would treat their offspring. The results were pitiful. One report showed that these mothers treated their young as large fleas infesting their bodies. They often attacked their offspring without provocation, biting and beating them and pushing their faces into the wire floors of their cages. Such experiments may eventually provide specific answers to many of man's behavioral problems.

There is a vast, and still untapped, store of data shared by apes and men which will help man understand himself better. Perhaps a significant contribution will be made by apes to the identification of underlying causes of man's phobias and mental illnesses. Few animals share the average man's fear of, or repulsion for, snakes. Does man with his dominant mental capacity learn to fear snakes, or is it instinctive?

Chimpanzees seem to have an almost universal fear of snakes. The sight of one usually sends them into hysterics. One chimp owner who occasionally handled a snake within sight of his pet had to submit his hands to the chimp's examination later. The chimp studied them closely, turning them over and examining every possible place where the snake could have bitten him.

Gerald Durrell told of a chimpanzee in his care that he kept chained in the camp clearing most of the day. Whenever the chimp spotted a snake, even a minute one, his hair immediately stiffened and he began moaning softly. If the snake came closer the chimp snatched up handfuls of grass or twigs and threw them at it.

One evening the chimp refused to enter his box where he customarily spent each night. This was unusual because he was always ready for this secure spot by nightfall. When Durrell tried to push him toward the box, the chimp took his hand and led him to the box before retreating and hooting in fear. The chimp pointed to the nest.

Durrell looked into the nest box and found a tiny, blind burrowing snake curled on the blankets and banana leaves. It was harmless but the chimpanzee did not come closer until the snake was removed.

Zoo keepers learned long ago that the best tool to use in moving apes in or out of a cage is a mechanical snake. Even adult gorillas will run from a mechanical snake. The next best weapon is a water hose. Although apes like to splash water from their drinking basins, they don't like an overall soaking.

Chimpanzees, as well as certain monkeys, have played a vital part in preparing man for space flight. What would happen to an astronaut if the pressurization in his space suit were to be destroyed abruptly during a space walk? The answer to this and many similar problems is under investigation at Holloman Air Force Base in New Mexico.

Chimpanzees there have been exposed to these situations in the laboratory and have shown that at least some of the basic concerns about danger to astronaut's bodies were groundless. Chimpanzees have been taken on simulated "space walks" in the lab and suddenly subjected to the complete vacuum a man would be subjected to if his space suit were punctured.

These chimpanzees underwent severe physical jolts. One literally inflated until breathing, heart functions and measurable brain activity stopped for two minutes. An hour after normal pressure had been restored, however, the chimp was himself again and performing the tasks given him. Chimps and monkeys provided scientists with answers for the best ratio of oxygen to use for astronauts.

As intriguing were experiments in performing vital tasks which must be done manually on space flights. Chimpanzees were rewarded with food bits which popped out of a slot when certain movements were done correctly. One of these included the difficult task of superimposing a drifting circle of light on to a stationary crossmark displayed on an electronic screen. The chimp had to move the circle with a universal control stick, almost as if it were flying an unsophisticated airplane by instrument.

By 1949, rhesus monkeys were taking rocket trips over eighty miles into the atmosphere and in 1961 the chimpanzee "Ham" made a suborbital flight. Ham was strapped into a one-ton Mercury-Redstone space capsule which was launched 155 miles into space, reaching speeds of 5,000 M.P.H.

Ham apparently enjoyed his ride immensely as well as the attention showered on him. A television camera was focused on his face during the entire flight. When his capsule was opened and he was unstrapped Ham stepped out smiling and shook hands with all the aplomb of any human astronaut who would follow the trail he had blazed. After chattering animatedly he ate an apple, lettuce and part of an orange. A real celebrity, Ham was retired to the National Zoological Park in Washington, D. C. Two years later, a chimp named Enos orbited the earth but later died of gastroenteritis.

Is such use of apes cruel? It would take an unknowledgeable, over-emotional person to consider it cruel. Chimps used in the space program have been given greater health care and provision for their needs than the large majority of humans on earth. Almost no dog or cat owners have the knowledge or facilities to afford their pets comparable care.

2: *Stalking Wild Chimpanzees*

THE BEST KNOWN CHIMPANZEE INVESTIGATOR IS A BRITISH girl, Jane Goodall, whose determination to do the work she wanted to led to her success, and has excited envy of girls throughout the world. An avid animal student as a child, she had lost none of her enthusiasm by the time she left school at eighteen and worked as a secretary long enough to accumulate the fare to Africa. This done she arrived in Nairobi in 1957 and shortly convinced anthropologist Dr. L. S. B. Leakey to hire her as his secretary.

Impressed by her determination to study animals, Leakey helped arrange financing for her to study chimpanzees in Tanzania's Gombe Stream Reserve on Lake Tanganyika. By mid-1960 she, her mother and a native cook began the chimpanzee study on a shoestring. Lacking adequate drugs, the two women were bedridden with malaria within sixty days. Although their condition was critical for a few days, the devoted cook ministered to them day and night.

Shortly after recovering, Jane saw her first chimpanzees. It was October and wild figs were ripe, a magnet for feeding chimpanzees. There was a grove above her lakeside camp and she began her observations, stationing herself where she could be seen by the chimpanzees coming and going. Soon they became accustomed to her presence and allowed her to move closer on successive days.

During the following years, the camp was made more serviceable as new funds were provided for her investigations. One important source was the National Geographic Society, which has reported Jane's work several times over the past few years. Of more importance to Jane was the Society's assignment of wildlife photographer Baron Hugo van Lawick to film her work. A young but experienced animal photographer, Hugo, of Dutch descent, assembled an invaluable film record of Jane's work.

After reporting to the National Geographic Society in Washington in 1964, Jane and Hugo stopped in London and were married before returning to their study of the chimpanzees.

The significance of Jane's chimpanzee researches stemmed from her manner of working. She settled herself down in chimpanzee habitat to observe them almost continuously over a period of years. This continuity allowed her to identify behavior which had not been suspected by past researchers whose limited time in study areas provided only passing observations of chimpanzee groups.

She discovered aspects of chimp behavior which had not been reported before. She saw them in stylized rituals and she experienced some chilling moments when there were doubts about her own safety.

Once while working through a wet forest she caught sight of a chimpanzee hunched on a low limb a few feet away. Stopping she pretended to be interested in her own possessions. A slight sound behind her revealed the presence of an adult chimp waiting there, then another sound to one side located one there. She was surrounded.

A chimp sounded a low "Hoo!" It was repeated by other chimps in thick vegetation around her. Then there was silence for a moment.

Suddenly the chimps screamed their belligerent "Wraa!" calls almost simultaneously and began shaking limbs and saplings violently, one so close that a branch bumped her head.

Thoroughly frightened, she waited until the terrifying screams subsided. After a few moments she looked about her and realized that the chimps had slipped away. When she climbed to her feet she found her weak knees barely able to support her.

At about the same time working in a heavily-jungled chimpanzee habitat, British zoologist Vernon Reynolds had less success. He was unable to habituate any group to his presence. After analyzing his experiences over eight months of observation he believed there were three reasons for this. One was the fact that there were usually three in the observation party, himself, his wife and a tracker. Another was the circumstance of chimpanzees in the sunlit upper limbs trying to distinguish the dark, suspicious figures on the forest floor. The most important reason, he felt, was the fact that each sighting was a different group of chimps, meeting these white faces for the first time and never having an opportunity to become accustomed to them.

Since the Budongo Forest of western Uganda where he made his observations was so large, Reynolds never had a chance to establish a rapport with a particular chimpanzee group. All groups were too mobile and too hard to locate in the heavy vegetation. Still he had many experiences which provided new information on the chimpanzee in the wild. His first encounter with chimps was a moment to remember. He and his wife were watching a chimp group move away when he found himself in a light rain. Glancing up he found a big male directly above urinating upon him. The incident was not unique. Reynolds later found himself in such light rains several times.

Shortly he found just how different a chimpanzee group can be from the retiring gorilla group which fades quietly into the jungle when alerted. After observing feeding chimpanzees for a few minutes Reynolds and his wife noticed a young adult ten yards to one side. It chewed leaves for a moment as it stared quietly. Suddenly it barked harshly, rocked back and forth on its sapling perch and leaped to the ground. Immediately it swung up a closer sapling still barking and shrieking.

Chimpanzees materialized from the surrounding vegetation and in moments Reynolds and his wife were encircled by shrieking chimps shaking limbs and saplings until the jungle seemed alive. A large limb, broken by too much chimpanzee weight, crashed to the ground behind them.

Forcing himself to remain calm Reynolds timed the outburst at six minutes. It subsided for a few seconds then swelled again. The chimps were working closer and there was no doubt that they were working themselves into a frenzy which seemed close to an assault. Reynolds looked at his terrified wife, took her hand and led her away quickly.

It may very well be that chimpanzees in their habitat are more dangerous to man than gorillas. Chimpanzees are much larger than is generally supposed since almost all chimps seen on television, in the movies, or in zoos are young, tractable animals which can be trained or handled with ease. Fully grown chimpanzees are seldom seen in these places because they are so difficult to handle and are often dangerous.

Vernon Reynolds was twice charged by adult chimpanzees with the result that he is not willing to abide by the advice to stop and calmly face the oncoming animal. He believes it is safer to step forward, shouting and threatening when a determined chimpanzee charges.

Once Reynolds and a tracker were charged by an adult male while they approached a group 100 yards away. Hearing noises a few steps ahead they looked up to see a large chimpanzee break cover and head for them in galloping leaps. His head, sunk deep into his shoulders, was down and his mouth was set in a scowl. The tracker stepped forward and swung his brush knife, or *panga,* and Reynolds swung his camera tripod at the ape. The chimp whirled and fled. Reynolds measured the skid marks where the chimp turned. They were only three paces away.

On another trip into the same area an adult female charged them. Hearing a chimp infant scream from a tree to one side, they looked toward it and saw the female with eyes fixed on them and charging. The two men prepared to defend themselves and the female braked to a halt five steps away before glaring momentarily and rushing back to retrieve her infant.

In areas where they are not hunted extensively chimpanzees are among the noisiest of jungle creatures, exceeded perhaps only by elephants screaming at evening watering places. Reynolds believes that their noisy movements through the jungle serve to intimidate lurking leopards or other potential ambushers. The noise twenty chimps can make is unbelievable, he reported, and when it is started by an exuberant chimp and taken up by others the bedlam may last for a considerable time.

When chimpanzee groups settle into an abundance of ripe fruit their screams and calls seem to serve the purpose of attracting distant chimps to the treasure. A thick grove of ripening figs or other fruit caused large numbers of chimps to gather, usually all those within two miles since chimp screams and calls can be heard this far. When food trees were scattered the chimps split into twos and threes as necessary to exploit these scattered sources. The chimpanzee's loose social organization seems best suited to exploiting the jungle fruits as they ripen at different seasons. Reynolds believes that adult males are the principal food finders.

In contrast gorillas, quiet and relatively intact as semi-permanent groups, found their food—leaves, vines, weed stalks—almost everywhere they moved in their chosen habitat. They had no reason to notify other groups of food finds since it was scattered everywhere.

A little-understood chimpanzee event is popularly called the carnival, or *ngoma* in Swahili. The event has been known to naturalists for over a century but the reasons for the performance are still conjectural. Often drumming plays a part, not by sticks on a log, but by chimp hands beating rapidly on the high, thin, buttressed roots of the ironwood tree. When two such roots are close together a natural sounding box is formed. Chimp drumming is not accidental or rare. They have been observed doing it many times.

The real carnival atmosphere is generated by chimpanzees screaming, however. Vernon Reynolds watched a carnival begin when a dozen feeding chimpanzees were joined by a similar group. For fifty-five minutes Reynolds watched the chimps rush about among the limbs screaming, swinging, leaping and shaking branches. None of the chimpanzees struck or bit each other although they frequently faced each other, turned away and resumed their screaming and leaping. After the noise subsided both groups resumed feeding for a time before wandering off together.

Although this particular carnival seemed no more than a greeting display it lasted an unusually long time. Reynolds reported many meetings of chimpanzee groups without any display. He heard the carnivals at all hours during his months in Uganda's jungles and learned in conversations with natives that all inhabitants of the area were familiar with these chimpanzee events, so much so that the local name for chimpanzee had the meaning "it beats."

Among the chimpanzee's strangest rituals is the reaction to rain. Jane Goodall saw the same stylized behavior by chimpanzees on four different occasions, each about noon and in the same type of terrain. Each ritual lasted less than a half hour but at least fifteen minutes. She called it a rain dance since she saw the routine first during a heavy rain. Apparently it does take place at other times when an appropriate trigger sets off the ritual. The trigger may have been the awareness that they were being watched by a person.

Jane had been watching sixteen chimps playing and feeding in a tree on a grassy slope across a ravine. Rain clouds had been heavy all morning and now rain began. The chimps climbed from the tree, sat for a time on the ground, then headed up the slope.

When they were close to the ridge crest one male turned and ran back down the hill, rearing to full height by a tree as he passed and tearing off a limb. He waved this briefly then dragged it behind him as he continued. Three more males followed his example, swinging up into a tree on the way down before leaping twenty-five feet to the ground and tearing off limbs on the way.

All the time rain fell, lightning and thunder were frequent and the apes screamed. When each male reached the bottom he turned to climb the slope and repeat the reckless downhill plunge. After about a half hour of this the chimp actors and chimp spectators in trees at the ridge top disappeared quietly over the crest.

Rain is received with varying behavior by different chimpanzees. Some get very excited and put on individual displays which build into wild dancing and smashing of vegetation. One old male began such a display while Jane sat on a banana box to protect its contents, threatened her with an upraised arm, then hit a tree, the box and Jane.

Displays appear often to be generated by an exciting change in the environment. Recently I watched an adult male in the Albuquerque Zoo stage such a display when about fifty small school children began screaming in an attempt to get a reaction. The reaction took the form of a vicious attack on the cowering female chimp in his enclosure. The children screamed louder. The male beat and bit the unfortunate target for his irritation until a guard arrived to silence the screaming children and send them on their way. The male chimp immediately calmed and turned away from the beleaguered female.

Most chimpanzees dislike rain because it leaves them miserable. They make no shelters and after becoming soaked under vegetation or tree trunks, move out into the downpour. Mothers sit hunched over their infants as the rain soaks through the long outer hairs. As water collects the chimps shake the water from their heads and when the rain subsides they may strip off handfuls of leaves to towel themselves as best they can.

Infants generally stay warm and dry huddled against

their mothers but juveniles don't have this protection. They get as cold and miserable as the adults, but after a rain they exercise until warm by running, jumping and doing acrobatics. One young chimp turned somersault after somersault on muddy ground until covered with mud and so dizzy that it had no choice but to continue sitting—unsteadily—in another cold rain shower.

Vernon Reynolds found that chimpanzees in western Uganda's jungles had home ranges of six to eight square miles and that in any range the population density was about ten to the square mile. In the single Budongo Forest area of 135 square miles there was a permanent chimpanzee population between 1,000 and 2,000.

Animal collector Heinrich Oberjohann, after years of observing the evening gathering of West African chimpanzees on their night nests, described a typical evening. Twilight brings an end to foodgathering and the small groups drift toward their nests. Suddenly a long "Hooee!" sounds. The scattered groups answer immediately and break into movement toward the nesting area which may be five to eight miles away. They swing hurriedly through the limbs as darkness gathers and each chimp hurries to get a choice nest.

When the nest area is reached, arguing chimpanzees sound as if they were having a pitched battle but seldom does one chimp touch another. It consists of bluffing, scolding and screaming, but the result is almost deafening to human ears.

Young males or mothers with infants already making

themselves comfortable in nests desired by old males are promptly expelled. If a young male is slow to respond he may receive a bite or blow.

By the time most noise has subsided there is a good chance that several chimps low in the order of dominance have no nests, and are in effect turned out for the night. Their cries of distress continue for a time. Only complete darkness silences this last noise.

Oberjohann suggests that the chimpanzees of West Africa's jungles use a number of night nesting areas, a tactic used by many wildlife species in areas of significant hunting pressure. In the chimpanzee's case the situation causes the frequent game of "musical nests," when some nests unused for weeks have fallen apart or become unsuitable and the chimpanzees compete for better nests. In addition the chimp group may have grown in numbers since the last visit with the result that there are not enough nests to go around.

For all practical purposes chimpanzees abandon nests after a single night's use or at least for a time. The nests serve no function as a home den or shelter from rain or wind.

The nest's only function is to serve as a sleeping platform. Monkeys have calloused pads on their buttocks which allow them to sleep comfortably sitting on a limb. However, chimpanzees are usually too heavy for high-limb sitting and they don't have fifth hands—tails—as do monkeys for support. Consequently, the chimp's nest provides a secure bed in high, thin limbs. Rarely is the nest made on the ground. The location in thin limbs serves as insurance against surprise attack by night-prowling leopards since its attempt to reach the nest, if it could climb to it at all, provides forewarning.

In West Africa, because of man's persecution, chimpanzees are particular about the site chosen for night nests. They use only the highest, straight-trunked trees hung with lianas which are used as ladders. Such trees are emergents from the jungle canopy and grow as scattered clumps, often three miles or so apart. The chimpanzees seek them out, preferring trees with suitable limbs at least one hundred feet above the ground.

Chimpanzees have an aversion to darkness. Vernon Reynolds watched chimps feeding during the last hour of daylight. They crammed fruits into their mouths with increasing speed and frequently glanced at the setting sun to see how much time was left for eating. Finally when the sun settled from sight chimps stuffed cheeks, piled as many extra fruits as possible into spare hands and hurried off to their nests.

Heinrich Oberjohann, who spent forty years in the West African bush country, found that each year there resulted in fewer sightings of animal life. There was one exception. Chimpanzees grew in numbers each year despite increasing efforts by native farmers to keep them out of their crops and to hunt them for meat. African guns, traps and snares have failed to slow their building numbers.

As in the case of the American coyote and the imported ringneck pheasant in midwestern grain fields, the effect of man on the environment has been good. His farming has provided food in abundance for some wildlife. In West Africa the adaptable chimpanzees have learned to use various tricks to distract farmers while they swarm into fields of maize and sugar cane, both crops which draw the chimps like magnets.

Chimpanzees occasionally become carnivorous predators eating small animals such as monkeys, young baboons, bush pigs, bushbuck, rodents and birds. Jane Goodall found remains of twenty-three animals in the digestive wastes of Gombe Stream chimps during one twelve-month period.

Baboon troops and chimps associate closely with each other in much of their habitat but the baboons must stay alert to a quiet gathering of hunting chimpanzees. Although the young of both species sometimes play together, adult chimpanzees view young baboons as items for the menu rather than companions. Jane Goodall saw the end of one hunting stalk when a chimpanzee seized a young baboon by a rear leg and swung it repeatedly against the ground. Later the successful hunter ate his fill, then abandoned the remains to begging companions, one of which later shared his portion with another outstretched chimp hand.

Chimpanzee hunts seem more like the product of chance than a deliberate hunt after unseen game. A young animal is spotted. Nearby chimp adults communicate to each other this fact, apparently by posture and attitude— as a pointer dog signals a bird hunter—and the chimps

converge on their target. If the target is a young baboon
it may elude the hunters long enough to sound a cry for
help and the baboon troop swarms in to stop the hunt
with much screaming and threatening. In a single encounter between an adult chimp and baboon the chimp
may be the victor but the chimpanzee group is no match
for the well-organized baboon troop.

In areas where chimpanzees and baboons are hunted
extensively the sight of an unarmed man is largely ignored
but the sight of a man carrying a gun sends them into a
panic. They have learned the rifle's danger. Heinrich
Oberjohann during years in the West African jungle saw
this happen repeatedly and chimpanzee mothers, which
would carry their young to safety under ordinary circumstances, shake themselves free of clinging young at the
sound of a gun and flee for their own safety. The abandoned young remain where they fall and scream their
woeful cries until they are picked up by captors or the
mothers return to them after the jungle quiets. Oberjohann once captured five chimpanzee young ranging in
age from one month to one year on successive collection
trips.

Chimpanzees ordinarily show limited fear of an unarmed man. If surprised by the appearance of a man
while they are in the trees the chimps hurry to safety. If
surprised on the ground, chimpanzee mothers tend to
remain calm and gather up their young before moving
off.

Joy Adamson, in her *Living Free*, told of an incident

with baboons which may have been misinterpreted. At one of her East African camps she had sketched and worked within a few yards of baboons repeatedly without any particular notice being taken of her by the baboons. One day when she saw a crocodile asleep nearby she got her rifle and headed for the river determined to kill this menace.

As soon as the baboon troop saw her with a rifle, however, they set up such an outcry that the crocodile escaped. Joy believed that the baboons were serving as lookouts for the crocodile and had warned it. The same thing happened the next day.

Observers of African apes will not accept this viewpoint. They believe the baboons were alarmed at the sight of the rifle.

Chimpanzees share a ritual with some monkey species which establishes dominance, cleanly and decisively. Two adult chimps meeting as strangers may use the ritual rather than go through various threats and bluffs.

Heinrich Oberjohann told of reestablishing the pecking order he had maintained with an adult chimpanzee he had kept several years before. By chance he found himself aboard a ship carrying a cargo of his animals to Europe when his former charge appeared on deck. The chimp, the property of a crewman, had been kept below decks for a considerable time and had been freed by accident.

In the next few moments of excitement, the chimp leaped atop a baboon cage, allowed a finger to intrude into the cage and promptly received a nasty bite. Shortly when Oberjohann asked the chimp to come forward so he could examine the wound the chimpanzee held his wounded hand behind and extended its other hand to identify the man's intentions.

The chimp's hand was held at eye level. Recognizing the gesture the man extended his left hand to the chimpanzee's open mouth and placed his fingers between the chimp's teeth. The chimp performed the same gesture. If neither bit the two would remain as friendly equals— but the chimpanzee was seeking a guardian just now to take care of its wound and to relieve it of the intolerable captivity below decks.

Oberjohann bit quickly while he jerked his own fingers free. Then he hit the chimpanzee full in the chest with his free hand, knocking it to the deck. Immediately the man danced upright around the prostrate chimp as one of its own species would do.

The chimp accepted the come-down immediately, whimpered and extended its arms to embrace its former foster father. From that moment the chimp was a gentle friend again.

Among the apes and many other primates one of the prerogatives of dominance is that all dominated members of the group show their recognition of a lesser status by grooming the dominant animals. The details of grooming have been in dispute among zoologists for some time. There is little doubt, however, that grooming serves several purposes.

The groomer usually picks off salty residues and puts

these in its mouth. Monkey and ape owners can be volubly indignant over a suggestion that their pets have fleas and ticks. As a matter of fact, all apes and monkeys are just as susceptible to bugs as animals or humans. One can seldom find a flea or tick on an ape or monkey, however, because grooming removes them almost as fast as they take up residence. Perhaps a basic purpose for all grooming is that it feels good. It massages the skin and serves to relax and calm, a situation of some importance to those low in the order of dominance when leaders are agitated.

As in humans and many other species in the animal kingdom, dominance is not necessarily a result of large size and strength. It may be achieved by bluffing, threatening or an alliance with a more powerful sponsor who will lend his protection in case the younger chimp gets himself into trouble by overstepping his bounds.

Jane Goodall told of one young adult male who came up with a unique way of achieving status. One day he seized an empty kerosene can and dragged it along behind him, making a noise so startling that other chimps hurriedly moved aside. Improving on a good thing the chimp learned to bat three empty cans along in front of him whenever he felt like shaking up his companions. So impressed were they by this un-jungle-like clatter that all the domineering males in the vicinity immediately came to him in submission. Jane watched one adult male that had dominated all around him for months come to the new leader, panting and bowing. The oldster kissed him, touched him, then began grooming him as assurance that he recognized the young male's new status.

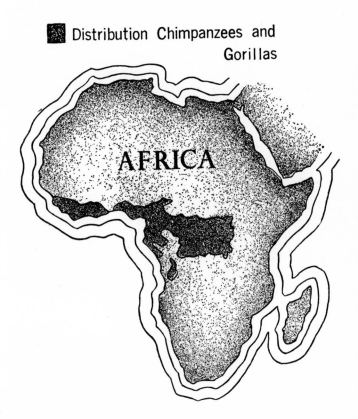

Distribution Chimpanzees and Gorillas

AFRICA

All of Africa's chimpanzees are not alike. The common chimpanzee is variously classified *Anthropopithecus troglodytes, Pan satyrus* and *Pan troglodytes.* A thinly-haired form, the bald-headed chimpanzee, has been classified *Anthropopithecus calvus* or *Pan calvus.* There is a dwarfed race, or species according to some taxonomists, which has been described in some detail by Desmond Morris of the London Zoo. It is the *bonobo* or pigmy chimpanzee, *Pan paniscus,* which is found in a small area south of the Congo River. In initial reports during 1929 it was considered a dwarfed black-faced race of the ordinary chimpanzee. Subsequent studies apparently have proved its distinctive identity as a species to be authentic.

It is more slender and only half the size of the ordinary chimpanzee. Ears are relatively small and the head is more spherical. It has a striking difference in personality from its larger relative. It is sensitive, but calm and seldom bites. Its language is completely different from that of the ordinary chimpanzee. Its mating behavior so closely resembles that of *Homo sapiens* that it is startling, and external reproductive organs in the female are significantly lower than those in the common chimp.

The bonobo is rare. Only eleven females and six males are known to be in zoos. Only one successful zoo birth through 1965 is known and apparently no studies of consequence have been made of the species in the wild. Because it is so man-like in behavior and physique it may very well be that this ape can tell us more about ourselves than any of the monkey kingdom.

Heinrich Oberjohann, whose background of chimpanzee knowledge included forty years of close association with them in West Africa, reports a race of chimpanzee in Togoland and the Congo which reach *average* heights of six feet when grown. They have a reputation for continual wandering through those areas farthest from man's activity. Oberjohann believes their mentality superior to that of other chimpanzees and for this reason they are more dangerous to man than other chimpanzees.

3: *Chimpanzee Family Life*

IT COMES AS A SHOCK TO THE ZOO VISITOR WHEN HE SEES A female chimpanzee in heat. The bare portions of her buttocks swell and become pink or red. To most of us viewing such a female ape or monkey the appearance suggests some abnormal growth or body condition which will soon bring about the animal's death. Few people become accustomed to this sight, yet it serves the vital purpose one week out of every five of alerting males that it is time to begin the reproductive process.

Strangely both chimpanzee and gorilla females usually initiate the courting process, even to the point of occasional harassment in order to get males to stop eating or napping long enough to pay attention to them. This situation is not true with baboons, or most other mammal species whose males are aggressive at mating time. This factor of casual response on the part of chimpanzee and gorilla males is probably the most serious threat to the perpetuity of both species in an environment eroded by man's activities.

In contrast the baboon, which is not credited with the

same mental capacity as either species, is able to thrive in a changing landscape of increasing human competition. Given this species' sexual and social aggressiveness, both ape species would have much larger populations today.

So pronounced are the periodic drives which overtake the female chimpanzee that she usually seeks out every available male in the vicinity before the drive has subsided. Then she has no more interest in the males except to stay out of their way while feeding or traveling.

When birth occurs the new mother allows the group to move off while she remains in her nest for several days. She has no interest in food or anything outside the nest but devotes herself entirely to the tiny infant. Her hand supports its neck at the back as it nurses at any hour of the day or night. For the first three or four days the infant is held at her chest almost continually.

At the end of this time she sets the infant in her lap where it burrows into her hair and behind her thighs until no part is visible except its head. For the next three to four months the mother carries her infant almost unseen by using one leg to hold it against her abdomen. Except for her hopping the casual observer has no indication that she has a new infant.

During this period the mother's movements are quieter than usual. There are no acrobatics and although she still travels through the trees much of the time, she takes care not to make any movement which might dislodge the infant.

At about four months old, the young chimp begins to notice objects beyond the mother's lap. Crawling bugs, falling leaves, birds and other chimps absorb its attention for longer periods but it has no inclination to leave the lap's security.

At this age the mother would not let the infant leave her lap if it wanted to do so. However, within a few more weeks she begins a frustrating process, pushing her infant away so she can be free of it temporarily. The young chimp rebels at this action and sets up such an outcry that she usually takes it back on her lap. This is repeated every day and the arguments become more prolonged. The young chimp is torn between two desires—to investigate the objects beyond his mother but also to remain in his secure place. When the mother tries to get him to "go out and play," it realizes it is being deprived of the lap and resists this temporary rejection with all its strength and voice.

At about the age of six months baby chimps take their first steps and shortly move a few yards away from their mothers. All adult chimps look on infants of this age with grandfatherly eyes. Crusty oldsters who will not tolerate other adults near them will gently pat these appealing infants.

Growing up has its problems for the young chimp. During its third year when the mother's milk stops, the growing youngster finds that adults become a little less tolerant, especially when it rushes up to grab a bite of food, a situation that caused no rebuffs while it was an infant. Now, however, it may be pushed away or shoved.

After a period of this, the mother relents for a while and senses the juvenile's confusion. It has come to her for

comfort and security, but her milk is gone and the be-
wildered youngster reverts temporarily to infanthood
for reassurance. It rides her back or suspends itself beneath
her. It is a strange sight because of the juvenile's size,
but the patient mother may allow her overgrown "baby"
a little more of this nuisance behavior until it adjusts to
its new place in chimpanzee society.

The juvenile begins learning what it can and cannot
do. If the mother is big and protective the youngster may
do a little bullying of older youngsters as long as the
mother is near to protect. As females grow into adolescence
at seven, they learn the necessity of treating adults of both
sexes with some respect. Any liberties such as sitting too
close to an adult or competing for particular food, may
bring on a quick rebuff. These young females keep away
from the young males their age because the latter, being
heavier and stronger, may attack. Young males also must
move and display with caution when near adult males
lest they invite an attack upon themselves.

Although not as closely knit a society as baboons and
with limited sense of social responsibility, there are instances of adoption of orphaned chimpanzee youngsters.
One situation admired by readers of Jane Goodall's *My
Friends the Wild Chimpanzees* was that of the little
chimp "Merlin" and his older sister. Merlin and his sickly
mother had not been seen for over two months when
Merlin and his older brother came into camp. Jane
watched the other chimpanzees in the vicinity greet him
profusely with hugs, kisses and grooming. After a time
the exhausted little chimp curled alongside his brother.

A few hours later his sister arrived. She scampered to her brother and as Jane described it, she appeared to adopt him at that moment. From that time he slept beside her at night and she watched over him as best she could. When it was time to go to another spot she waited for him before moving.

For weeks this adoption seemed to work well. Merlin seemed as contented as other chimps his age. Unfortunately, his sister's attentions were not enough. By the time he was three Merlin was physically stunted, introverted and neurotic. He showed nervous habits common to chimps in captivity, rocking from side to side and pulling out his hairs to nibble at the roots.

Young chimpanzees, like their human counterparts, have their problems of loneliness, boredom, low moments and high moments. One Gombe Stream Reserve three-year-old, finding herself abandoned by habitual playmates because of circumstance, began romping with a female baboon juvenile about her age. The playmate situation was not uncommon since the young of both species often played together but after a time these two went to some trouble to find each other. On one occasion the young chimpanzee was observed high in a tree watching a baboon troop a quarter mile distant.

Shortly a small baboon left the troop. The young chimp swung to the ground immediately and rushed to meet her playmate. The two hugged each other and pressed their faces together before beginning a romp of wrestling and tickling each other. Such occasional play lasted for months until the fast-growing baboon grew too old to enjoy play.

Christine, the baby chimp reared by photographer Lilo Hess, threw some light on the reason a chimpanzee mother is not apt to leave her infant behind when she decides to move off into the jungle. Miss Hess often took Christine out to play in the yard where she climbed ropes, played on a swing and explored much as a chimp infant would in its jungle habitat. Miss Hess had to sit close to the play area or Christine would not play.

Regardless of what the little chimp was doing she seemed always to have one eye on her foster parent and seemed to sense when Miss Hess was thinking about leaving. When Miss Hess stood to leave Christine immediately gave an alarmed cry and rushed to her.

Chimpanzee families and human families have much in common. When a second infant comes along the older chimp youngster often shows its resentment and jealousy. Jane Goodall watched one young chimp—slightly crippled at birth—express its unhappiness by whimpering at its mother's heels during every movement. When the mother sat down to groom or nurse her new infant the youngster sat down at some distance and never showed any particular affection for the infant.

In contrast Jane frequently observed an older sister's fascination with a new brother. Whenever the mother would sit down the older sister stopped playing or eating to hurry over and stare at her new brother or to reach out and touch him. For weeks she tried to take him but her mother pushed her away or otherwise stopped this effort.

At the age of thirteen weeks, however, the new brother

was allowed in the arms of his sister. She pulled him gently to her with one foot and held him quietly in her arms for a few moments. When he whimpered his mother quickly took him. Finally the mother chimp allowed her daughter to take the infant away to play as long as the daughter remained within sight.

As more weeks passed the daughter almost assumed the duties of a foster mother. She carried him about when she was not playing or eating and if another young chimpanzee approached to play with the infant, she put on an angry display to drive it away. By the age of thirty months she had lost much of her possessive interest and played with him occasionally when he was not playing with other juveniles of his age.

Males are physically mature by eight years and females, at ten. The females are ready to give birth to young now, but the males have two or three more years to go before they are accorded "social" maturity, or a reasonably high status in the chimpanzee pecking order. The males eventually reach weights of up to 175 pounds and heights of almost six feet, the females, less. Both reach ages of about forty if allowed to live out their normal life spans.

The chimpanzee group is a fluid organization. A mother and her several offspring of different ages form the most permanent group. Occasionally other matriarchal groups join for a day or so if traveling or feeding. The independent —adult—males join casually. Only when a large grove of ripening figs or other fruit attracts many chimpanzees do large groups form. This may last for days since an area of fruiting trees usually has other groves of the same species in neighboring similar terrain. The older chimpanzees are aware of these locations and travel between them, still as loosely-knit groups.

A considerable amount of information about chimpanzee psychology and behavior must be accumulated before large-scale raising of chimps in captivity can be successful. To most of us the obvious answer would be to place an adult male with an adult female and let nature take its course. Unfortunately the course nature takes in such instances is often erratic.

Armand Denis found in beginning his Florida chimpanzee farm that many chimps cannot tolerate each other in captivity. Almost half of his females had a strong dislike of all males from the beginning. An even higher proportion of males could not stand to be in the same cage with females. Many males would attack females immediately when the two were placed together. Even those males which would mate with females as calmly as free-living chimps often attacked the females immediately after mating.

Many captive chimp births were circumvented by miscarriages. Normal births often posed confusing problems to the mothers who were "haphazard" in the care of their offspring. Mothers laid their infants on the floor and forgot them. Some mothers did not have enough milk to provide adequate nutrition. In one case a chimpanzee mother gave birth to twins—an extremely rare circumstance—and although she seemed completely absorbed in them she could not seem to pay attention to both simultaneously. While she nursed and fussed over one, she abandoned the other on the floor. When the latter's cries grew loud and pitiful, she dropped the twin in her arms and picked up the crying infant.

This was enacted over and over and the infants lost weight steadily. Finally after much effort the keepers separated her from her babies. Although almost past recovery they did respond to round-the-clock treatment and survived as bottle-fed infants. The mother promptly forgot her infants.

4: *Apes as Pets*

ANIMAL COLLECTOR GERALD DURRELL, WHOSE KEEN OBSER-
vation of animal behavior and humorous perception have
made his animal books universally popular, once purchased an African planter's pet chimp named Charlie.
Because Charlie had spent more time in closer association
with man than his own kind he had a unique understanding of man's ways. He was as skilled an actor as any
devious small child and when caught in the act of doing
something he knew was apt to bring his master's frown
he pretended to know nothing of the cause.

During his daily exercise periods of freedom Charlie
usually sidled about for a time before casually snatching
a bunch of bananas from a table and racing for a tree. If
a man chased him, Charlie dropped the bananas, sat
down with his back to the pilfered fruit and assumed the
"picture of injured innocence." When the stolen fruit was
held before him, Charlie looked at it with surprise. Durrell
said that the chimp's face was so expressive that he could
carry on a long conversation without making a sound.

Durrell also purchased a female chimp, Mary, about the

same time who must have been teased and treated badly during her captivity. She could not tolerate anybody, black or white, touching her and at times she was vicious. Determined to win her friendship, Durrell treated her with kindness and gave her the best of food. She reacted positively and soon developed a wonderful, warm disposition. She loved sunning on a cross bar. When someone would step to the cage and blow on her she shrieked with laughter, sometimes until she was almost hysterical.

Mary carried one memory with her from her unhappy past. She exacted retribution from all black Africans, doing stunts and performing until they stepped close to her cage. Then her hand flipped out to rip off any clothing she could reach. This done she jumped around her cage in triumph waving her torn trophy.

Perhaps Durrell's most lovable chimp was a baby male purchased from a native hunter. Although tiny the little chimp was old enough to cause mischief. Consequently, the chimp, later named Chum, had to be caged except when someone could play with him or at least keep an eye on him.

The highlight of the day for Chum was the first hour of the day. As in much of Africa morning tea is a time-honored custom. When he was released from his cage at this hour Chum scurried across the floor and leaped into bed with Durrell to give him a juicy kiss. Then he sat alongside the man, murmuring happy grunts while Durrell poured tea, milk and much sugar into Chum's own mug.

Seizing the mug Chum stuck his face into it and drank

off the top noisily. Then he lifted the mug and drank every drop, before turning the mug over his head until the wet sugar slid into his mouth. Now he handed the mug back hoping for a refill.

When tea was over Chum began his morning games. First he would crawl down to the end of the bed and sit down long enough to make certain Durrell was watching. Then he would slide his cold hand under the sheet and seize one of Durrell's toes. When Durrell lifted himself in feigned indignation, the little chimp scurried across the room giggling.

When Chum was ready for another game he would crawl cautiously up the bed and study Durrell's face for a moment before yanking his hair and leaping for the foot of the bed. If he caught him, Durrell placed his hands next to the little chimp's neck to knead the collar bones until Chum was giggling and rolling hysterically.

These are among the most satisfying experiences of pet owners with young chimps. Other chimp owners, although experienced animal handlers, have had dismal experiences. One was in the West African jungles when a nine-month-old female came into a collector's hands. The first night she pressed herself tight against his chest and he was reassured that she had accepted him as a foster parent and he would have little trouble rearing her successfully.

In the middle of the night, however, she made a mess of the bed. The disgusted chimp owner got up to clean himself and the bed. The baby chimp rebelled at his attempt to set her down, digging her nails into his neck skin as he pulled her away forcefully.

He was unprepared for the endurance required to rear the chimp. Her cries grew so intolerable he refused to pick her up. After a few days she would not drink and her constant howling changed to wails. She died shortly.

Very few people have the tolerance and patience necessary to rear a chimpanzee. The young chimpanzee is far more demanding of time and affection than any human infant. A human mother feeds and tends to her baby, then sets it in a crib to spend most of the day alone.

The young chimpanzee cannot take such detached treatment. In the wild, it remains in its mother's arms continually and if she tries to set the baby chimp down a little arm reaches out quickly to grab her. The infant chimp is not mentally prepared for its mother or foster parent to set it down and leave it. Heinrich Oberjohann adopted many orphaned chimp babies. As soon as he extended arms of affection to any tiny chimp it pressed against his chest, pinching his skin hard enough to lacerate it.

Perhaps more than any other animal the chimpanzee integrates itself into the human race if adopted before it is a year old. It seems to forget its mother immediately and extends its affection to its new parent if he is knowledgeable enough in chimpanzee ways to merit it. Like a child, the young chimp begins imitating the gestures of its parent and tries futilely to reproduce the human sounds it hears.

There appears to be one necessity in training young chimps or children. They can be persuaded ultimately only by judicious use of corporal punishment. Although anger is undesirable as a motivation for administering punishment, chimp misbehavior must be stopped with immediate and deliberate punishment. If this seems unjustified the foster parent to a chimp need only study the reports of scientific observations of chimpanzee groups in their natural habitat. A mother chimpanzee administers punishment quickly and severely for such minor misbehavior as responding too slowly to her command.

Many animals have an empathy toward children which they do not extend to adults. The chimpanzee is no exception. An unmanageable adult chimp may be stopped short by a child's smile and led passively away. Heinrich Oberjohann told of one chimpanzee which had survived years of mistreatment by various owners. A teen-age girl who did a circus act with her father captured the chimp's affection with a gentle hug and it performed tirelessly in the act with her for over a year until the girl's mounting scoldings made him balk at performing further. Then the chimp became enraged when an adult picked up a stick as a threat. A serious situation was averted when a five-year-old girl took the big chimpanzee by the hand and led him away. His loyalty immediately shifted to her.

Meals are the highlights of the day for a chimpanzee in the jungle or in man's habitat. One chimp owner found that when meal preparations began the chimp could not contain itself. It insisted on helping set the table and making sandwiches. It could spread butter on a bread slice and arrange cold meats and cheese upon it almost as neatly as its owner. However, when the meal began the chimpanzee swept its upper lip like a vacuum cleaner over the bread to clear it of meat. Then it held the bread slice out for more. If the man did not replace the meat slice, the chimp helped himself.

Table clearing was this chimp's special job. It carefully brushed the table and dishes free of left-overs—and into its mouth.

By the time chimps are a year old their curiosity is almost insatiable. Any objects such as a can, bottle or glass which has been used in feeding is a magnet. The young chimp must know what it contains and if a few drops of liquid remains in a bottle the chimp must turn it up and swallow it. Few liquids are disdained. Gasoline— capable of burning human tissue without being set aflame —seems to have no adverse effect on the digestive tracts of chimps. Heinrich Oberjohann reported chimpanzees acquiring a taste for gasoline and drinking as much as a glassful daily. The apparent effect was beneficial since the gasoline rid them of intestinal parasites. Numbers of children, however, have died from the effects of swallowing kerosene or gasoline.

Chimpanzees have a predilection for mischief which can drive an owner to distraction. Oberjohann, after spending four decades with chimpanzees in their jungle en-

vironment, as well as his camps and homes, had ample
opportunity to watch numberless year-old chimps work
so hard at imitation that they became nuisances.

He told in his book *My Best Friends Are Apes* of cook-
ing soup in a large sauce pan set over a campfire while
five chimpanzees, who had the run of the camp, watched.
He lifted the lid and added salt. As he stirred the soup
one stepped up and reached for the ladle to help. He was
turned away. Another brought a jam can filled with dirty
water to add to the soup. Oberjohann stopped him and
found himself in an argument. When this was settled he
reached for his salt again, but he found the shaker empty
because another chimp had emptied it into the soup.

Oberjohann devised various ways to combat one chimpanzee's sly pilfering after he found his sugar bowl and
tobacco jar empty and several bottles of wine gone. He
ground an animal horn and mixed this with his tobacco.
The chimp stuffed his pilfered pipe with this, took one
puff and was nauseated immediately. A wine bottle was
filled with gasoline and put in its accustomed place. The
chimpanzee swallowed a mouthful and heaved. Oberjohann slowed its misery by making it take several glasses
of milk.

Still continuing its food pilfering the chimp watched
the man fill the sugar bowl but did not know that salt
instead of sugar was used. The man soon stepped out of
the room to the impatient chimpanzee's delight. As soon
as he closed the door Oberjohann bent down and looked
through the keyhole. Shortly he saw the chimpanzee

hurry to the door and peek through the keyhole to see if the coast was clear. Then the chimp hurried to the sugar bowl and emptied it into its mouth.

Oberjohann immediately opened the door. The surprised chimp dropped the sugar bowl and swallowed the salt. The man kept his face straight as the chimp's face showed its discomfort. Its mouth popped open. Its tongue pushed out and the chimp began whimpering. Oberjohann again stopped the shock to the chimp's stomach by giving it milk.

It seems that chimpanzees living in close contact with a man often develop a perception of his thoughts which borders on the uncanny. Although some indication in the way of the man's action suggests clearly to the alert chimpanzee what is about to take place, the man is usually unaware of making any such move. The situation is much like a pet dog sensing that his master is preparing to leave.

Oberjohann told of one unusual chimp which had so adjusted himself to man's way of life that he constantly sought activities to assure his master that he was human, too. The chimp slept in Oberjohann's tent as if he were a full partner in the man's animal collecting venture. Numerous tasks such as feeding animals and cleaning their cages were assigned the chimpanzee and he performed them well.

When porters were assembled for an animal collecting trip, the chimpanzee was well aware of what was about to take place and insisted on going along. He rolled his own blanket and joined the porters. The man tried to discourage him but the chimp insisted and the man finally agreed. The chimpanzee was allowed to carry a wicker basket with his makeshift hat thrown into it. The pace was almost too much and the chimp fell far behind as he tried to carry his basket on his head like the porters. Finally he moved the basket to his back and had no trouble maintaining the pace.

The chimpanzee infant, Christine, reared by Lilo Hess was as attached to her blanket as most human infants. She carried it, dragged it and wrapped it around her for days at a time without relinquishing her grip. At six months Christine loved baby toys. A rattle made in ring form was a favorite, as well as stuffed toys, especially a teddy bear. The teddy bear was a constant companion for months. She hugged it, kissed it, used it for a pillow, rolled on it while giggling or banged its head on the floor. Finally she poked an eye out and promptly lost her attachment for it. A stuffed dog soon took its place. A rubber mouse which squeaked when pressed scared her, but after several weeks she accumulated courage to touch it and soon carried it about in her mouth.

A memorable moment for the little chimp was the day Miss Hess brought a kitten to Christine. When Miss Hess opened the box and Christine saw the kitten she could hardly contain herself. Christine picked up the kitten and hugged it, sniffed it, then kissed it until it purred. After a few moments Christine set the kitten down carefully and went to other toys.

Although she played roughly with the kitten at times,

she liked to tuck it under an arm and curl up for a rest. When a bowl in which cake or frosting had been mixed was set before the two and the kitten moved toward it, Christine shoved the kitten's head aside and used an ear as a handle to hold it aside while she ate from the bowl.

During rough play the kitten began using her claws on the little chimp and occasionally giving her a number of scratches. Finally Christine learned to retaliate by biting the kitten's tail.

Miss Hess discovered fascinating little details of chimpanzee behavior as a result of rearing Christine. The chimp's sleep always seemed busy with dreams. She laughed or sucked noisily while she slept and on occasion burst out with terrified screams without awakening herself.

A number of knowledgeable animal collectors have managed to do a remarkable job of communicating with chimpanzees, even those straight out of the jungle. One example of this happened in 1955 when a Belgian government official in the Congo, Jean-Pierre Hallet, purchased a wounded adult chimp out of sympathy for the animal's condition. It had been caught three days before during a hunt. The chimp's supporting limb broke and he fell to the ground where natives threw a hunting net around him. When the chimp worked an arm free and grabbed a native, the latter chopped at it with a machete. The wound became infected.

Hallet and a helper carried the 150-pound chimp into the garage of his house near Lake Tanganyika and Hallet sent his helper out before locking the door. Hallet now sat down by the chimp and with words and gestures tried to make the chimp understand that he wanted to help. Hallet pointed to the net and to his knife in his effort to let him know that he would cut him free. Then Hallet patted the big chimp's head and gave him a kiss on the nose. The surprised chimp hooted quietly.

Now Hallet cut the net away from the wounded arm and examined the ill-smelling wound. Although the chimp winced from pain as the man handled the swollen hand and fingers, the chimp gave no indication of alarm.

Hallet carefully cut the net layers until the big chimp was standing free. The chimp stood motionless for moments, adjusting to the freedom, then began hooting with lips extended. Finally he quieted and gave Hallet a "suave, diplomatic smile." Hallet imitated the hoots as best he could, as well as the smile.

The chimp now hobbled forward, his legs still cramped from the long stay in the tight net, looked at his wounded arm and pointed to the wound. Hallet extended his hand and the chimp rested his swollen hand in the man's palm, grunting softly as he did so. Hallet examined the wound again for several moments, his examination mimicked by the chimp's stares.

When Hallet arose to go into his house and get his medical kit he attempted to close the garage door behind him. The chimp screamed his unhappiness and rushed to the door, trying to force it open and managing to insert his wounded arm into the crack. When the man opened the door slightly to free the chimp's arm, the latter shoved it open and rushed outside.

The chimp did not stop for 200 feet. Then he sat down screaming. Each time Hallet approached the chimp moved farther away. Finally the chimp allowed him to come up and take his healthy hand and lead him back to the garage.

There Hallet set him down and tried to make the chimp understand that he must leave temporarily, but each time he arose to leave the chimp did so, too. Hallet pushed him down and talked some more. After an hour of this Hallet managed to convince the chimp that he must stay there. He left and locked the door from the outside. The chimp began crying.

Hallet phoned a veterinarian immediately but learned that the man would not return until the next day. Gathering up his own medicinal supplies he returned to the garage to find the chimp waiting behind the door. When he opened it, however, the chimp did not try to escape but turned and walked submissively to his corner.

Hallet washed the wound with antiseptic as gently as he could and when he was almost finished the suffering chimp pulled his arm away. The chimp inspected the wound, holding it close to his eyes, then laid his hand back in the man's hand in "complete confidence."

After an application of sulfa powder Hallet wrapped the wound with gauze. Leaving he found no opposition from the chimp but upon looking back into the garage a moment later he found the chimp trying to remove the gauze. Hallet spoke firmly and tapped him on the cheek. The chimp began crying but left the bandage in place.

The next morning Hallet changed the bandage and fed

the chimp, but when he started to leave this time, the chimp pulled him back down. Wondering what the chimp wanted Hallet sat down and the lonesome chimp showed his satisfaction with pleased grunts. The man remained in place and dozed off but was awakened by fingers exploring his face.

Opening his eyelids only enough to see what was going on Hallet watched the chimp feel every bump and hole on his head. The chimp pulled each of his lips out to examine the man's teeth but when he tried to push a finger up Hallet's nose the latter stopped the exploration.

Still showing amazing trust, the big chimp laid his hand, palm up, in the man's lap and Hallet reciprocated by clasping it. The chimp went to sleep then for hours.

When the veterinarian arrived he found that the chimp had gangrene and that there was no alternative to amputation. The only practical solution for the chimp's future welfare was to take him to an animal research station where the operation could be performed and the chimp could live comfortably while scientists studied him. The station was over 200 miles distant. Hallet took him there in a pickup truck, a ride the chimp tolerated without complaint after Hallet persuaded him to get into the vehicle.

When he drove into the research station several surprised native workers, seeing the chimp sitting in the cab, sprinted for the safety of the buildings. After short negotiations Hallet turned the chimp over to the station's staff.

As he turned to go a profound moment occurred, as

Hallet reported it in his book *Congo Kitabu*. Instinctively he stuck out his left hand to shake the chimp's healthy left hand. The chimp had known Hallet for only two days but it was a parting of firm friends. The ape clasped the man's hand.

Although this almost too human-like behavior seems to some animal behaviorists as nothing more than anthropomorphism—assigning human behavior to animals—apparently it was just what it seemed to be. Handclasps, hugs, back-slapping, and extending a hand in friendship or submission are all characteristic of the chimpanzee as a species. A handshake—or the next thing to it—means about the same to chimpanzees as it does to humans.

Heinrich Oberjohann believes that chimpanzees never really accustom themselves to captivity, even in the best air-conditioned zoo enclosures where they are given constant veterinary care. Many animals are quite content with the constrictions of zoo life, but not the active, wide-ranging chimpanzee.

Young chimpanzees can seldom survive captivity in a cage. The deprivation of motherly affection with no suitable substitute causes the average chimp infant to lose its will to live and it dies. Recent studies of monkey infants reared under laboratory conditions without a mother or mother-substitute such as a playmate, grow into neurotic adults and never overcome this lack.

In chimpanzee country native Africans, who look on them merely as meat for eating, dislike to capture a chimpanzee younger than two years of age, since it is too small for roasting. If an adult chimp is captured, instead of being killed by the meat-eating natives immediately, it is kept alive long enough to be fattened for the pot.

At age two a chimpanzee adapts itself well to captivity but by four years it is nearly too old to become accustomed to its deprivation of liberty. Few chimpanzees captured at seven or older can tolerate cage life.

Captivity increases the chimpanzee's susceptibility to colds and respiratory diseases. Oberjohann said he has examined several hundred chimpanzees soon after capture and never found a single case of colds or scabies, although many showed scars from fights or accidents. However, close contact with man and cage life almost invariably brought on colds. Skin diseases commonly developed on captive chimps, and were more prevalent in equatorial than in temperate climates. Chimpanzees brought to Europe or America usually are soon rid of these diseases.

Gerald Durrell, whose animal collecting experiences were similar to Oberjohann's, once took possession of a grown chimp from an African friend to take it to an English Zoo. Durrell had a busy time of it during his first day with the big chimp, even having to strike him with a small withe to prevent the chimp from killing captive monkeys by throwing rocks at them.

By nightfall when Durrell brought the chimp's food and drink, the latter jumped up and down hooting with pleasure. Before he touched any of the food, however, he reached for the man's hand and pulled it to his mouth where he gently bit the fingers in the chimpanzee's way of showing friendship.

In years past baby gorillas have been kept occasionally as pets, chiefly by European officials and tradesmen in the Congo. These tiny gorillas accepted these unnatural habitats and adapted themselves to human family life.

Members of the American Museum-Columbia expedition were surprised at the intelligence of Alfred, a three-year-old gorilla belonging to a Greek merchant in a Congo jungle town. Alfred loved people and when market days brought large numbers to town Alfred played in front of the store all day entertaining appreciative natives. When he was not showing off he played with a small boy or rested in the arms of one of the store employees. He wore a one-piece jumper suit which apparently indicated to the little gorilla that he was no different from the other youngsters playing on the street. He usually made a mess of the suit, however, when drinking milk from his special tin cup. This was done while leaning out from a post with only one hand free to hold the cup and with no regard to milk cascading past his lip corners to splash over him.

One of the earliest attempts to do serious research on gorillas was the 1929 expedition sponsored jointly by the American Museum of Natural History and Columbia University. Even at this relatively recent date gorilla knowledge was scant and although many gorilla skulls and skins had found their way back to trophy rooms and museums, there had been no real effort to preserve whole gorillas for detailed study. This expedition under William K. Gregory of the Museum and Henry C. Raven of Columbia obtained permits to collect both mountain and lowland gorillas.

Although these men were world authorities on anatomy, paleontology, and zoology, practically no knowledge had accumulated on ape psychology and behavior. From time to time they had opportunities to buy young gorillas being reared almost as children by native Africans or European tradesmen. The scientists were perplexed when these young gorillas howled pathetically upon being placed in cages for transportation.

One eighteen-month-old female had been a member of a Belgian official's household which included numerous pets such as parrots and mongooses. The little gorilla had her own pet kitten which was usually treated with much gentleness and affection. Consequently when the scientists placed her in a strong slatted cage by herself she "screamed terribly." This unfortunate situation was alleviated partially during the first part of the trip out of the Congo jungle when one of the scientists sat by her cage feeding her bananas and oranges to keep her quiet.

On a train where she was shut in a baggage car she screamed at every stop until one of the men rushed back and stuck his fingers inside for her to grasp securely. When it was time to continue, the man had to disengage his fingers from the sobbing infant and return to a passenger car.

Finally on board a river steamer an African boy was

The baby gorilla GOMA

hired to take care of her day and night. She immediately quieted and sat contentedly on his lap.

Ivan Sanderson once lived near a London top floor apartment whose lady owner had a gorilla as a virtual member of the household. He was never restrained or caged in any way and acted the part of a human. Sanderson was amazed to see him step from a taxi one afternoon, as casually as any shopper. Sanderson watched him at play on many occasions and saw him exhibit only one non-human mannerism. The exception occurred when the gorilla dashed out of a French window and up to the roof where he sat and stared at the gathering crowd below. When half grown the gorilla was placed in the London Zoo where he lived in a large outdoor enclosure once housing lions. Here a small boy was his companion for play each afternoon, an activity which delighted zoo-goers.

Apparently the inclination toward playful mischief is as strong in the young gorilla as in chimpanzees, or in kittens and puppies. I watched an apprehensive little three-year-old female gorilla soon after she was placed in an enclosure with two four-year-old males at the Albuquerque Zoo. She kept them at a respectful distance with snarls and bared teeth.

This usually was effective in keeping the young males away from her whenever one approached too close. However, she was never quite prepared for retaliation when the male turned away, seemingly cowed by her threats. At this instant the male threw out a long arm and managed to slap her soundly on her rump before scurrying away.

Such retaliation is not limited to the young. After many enjoyable visits to Washington's National Zoological Park no scene quite eclipsed the afternoon I saw an adult male and female in their air-conditioned enclosure during a moment of family life. The female sat down on the floor and leaned against the wall to nap. The male decided this was an excellent idea. He sat down beside her, leaned over and plopped his head into her lap for a more comfortable nap.

The female had no sympathy for this inconvenience. She stood and dumped his head by letting it slide off her knees. Crossing the enclosure she sat down against the opposite wall and started her nap anew.

The male waited only until she was well settled before repeating his action, this time dropping his head into her lap with some finality. She straightened to her feet immediately, but the male's patience had worn thin. Before she took a full step one of his hands caught her solidly under her hips with a smack which could be heard through the double glass. This ended any inclination of either to nap for the time being. Both turned to other activities.

Unfortunately, few people are qualified to keep monkeys or apes as pets. Although many monkeys, and on occasion the two African apes, can be happy and healthy in the companionship of people such an alliance is a poor substitute for a life in a natural environment, or at least in a zoo or research station where a strong effort is made to duplicate the natural habitat.

Emotion has never been a substitute for knowledge in a pet owner. A baby chimp or gorilla is irresistible to most of us, children or adults, just as a baby is treated with tolerance and often affection by adult animals of many species. A baby chimp in a pet shop captivates almost every spectator and the emotional tug generated soon steers a person to the cash register and the chimp changes hands.

Then the baby ape owner begins discovering an awesome series of facts. Baby children can be laid down and ignored for hours at a time. Baby apes cannot. The mothers of both African apes carry their infants at their chest or abdomen every minute of the twenty-four hour day for weeks. The little ape cannot be laid down for a nap. Its fingers must grasp its mother or foster mother. It must feel her warmth and have contact-comfort. Although the physical tie with the mother ended with the breaking of the umbilical cord there is still a very real essence of life coming from its mother. It must be close enough to feel her pounding heart, to smell her, to feel her hair, to touch her mammary glands, to sense the security of her exclusive interest in her offspring.

Deprived of one or more of these factors the infant ape may survive. It may even develop into a normal adult. The chances are strong, however, that it neither survives nor develops into a normal adult. Sooner or later it may quit eating when its emotions are disturbed or its foster parent leaves it for a few hours or days.

An unfortunate fact that most of us prefer to forget is that every time a young ape is bought by a zoo or an individual, the natives of chimpanzee and gorilla country are encouraged to capture more infants for sale. Nor is there any way around the fact that almost every chimp or gorilla brought from the jungle was secured by killing the mother so her baby could be captured. Few of us looking at zoo apes allow our thoughts to drift back to brutal deaths in the jungle.

This situation may or may not continue in coming years. Larger zoos and research stations are accumulating knowledge on raising apes in captivity. Eventually all zoo apes may come from captive parents. However, that day is years away.

5: *Paintbrushes and Tools*

A SCIENTIST OBSERVING CHIMPANZEES ONCE WATCHED A chimp sit quietly for a quarter hour while it stared into the sunset. It did not drop its gaze nor move until the sun disappeared. This observation may have been the single most significant indication of ape mentality. Apes may share with man esthetic satisfactions never before suspected.

A relatively new exploration into ape mental processes is concerned with this. The ability of chimps and gorillas to compose balanced pictures has been investigated in some detail. Chimpanzee art has been found to be more solid than some products of human artists whose outputs are concerned primarily with sensationalism.

The chimpanzee cannot draw or paint realistic representations of objects but it can demonstrate an awareness of composition and design which is impressive. It can do such a good job of applying colors and forms to canvas that abstract art judges have unknowingly awarded competition prizes.

A college professor's wife, newly caught up in her

latest fad of learning "abstract" painting, became highly indignant when I mentioned chimpanzee abstracts receiving important exhibition prizes. "Impossible!" she stormed, but the facts speak for themselves. Some chimpanzee paintings and much abstract human art are only as good as the fluency of the critic describing them. Almost any mood or clue to behavior can be rationalized into such art work.

Can a chimpanzee paint a good picture? Yes, it can if we accept a definition of good art as a painting someone enjoys day after day. If such a painting is more enjoyable to Mr. Jones than a Picasso, then for all practical purposes the chimpanzee painting is superior esthetically to Picasso's work in the viewpoint of Mr. Jones.

With tongue in cheek we might consider that some chimpanzee "artists" are far more successful as professionals than some human artists. I have been drawing steadily since second grade but I have never sold art work at prices paid for chimpanzee paintings done at the Albuquerque Zoo recently. The "successful" chimp artists had no interest in the fact that their paintings earned several thousand dollars and paid for gorilla acquisitions by the zoo. The chimpanzees painted because the process was fun. There were no tricks involved in an attempt to fool the buyers. The payments—almost donations—were made a little easier by receipt of the unique paintings.

A chimpanzee's painting may seem to be nothing more than play. However, it is more than that because it develops with practice. A Russian zoologist Kotts found that initial pencil scribbles by a young chimpanzee, and later by her son of a similar age, consisted of long sweeping lines. Later pencil work by the chimpanzee showed lines of varying width and large numbers of crossed lines, a step showing improving visual control.

Desmond Morris, Curator of Mammals at London's Zoological Society, has studied chimpanzee painting extensively and has carried out numerous experiments with one chimp named Congo.

Congo's introduction to art came when a paper and pencil were handed to him at the age of eighteen months. He was allowed to discover for himself that a pencil would mark the paper and when Congo found this result an immediate interest was aroused. He scrawled and scribbled until the paper was covered.

In successive sessions, Morris realized that Congo was keeping his scribbling inside the paper's boundaries and producing a fan-like pattern. When a smaller sheet was given him Congo made a smaller pattern of scribbles to keep them on the paper.

Eventually Congo was given paints but he wanted to mix all the paints until they formed a single muddy brown. To get some insight on chimp response to different colors Morris dipped the brush into a color and handed it to Congo. When the brush was dry Morris handed him another.

One of the most important observations of Congo's painting was that it was not motivated by hope of reward. The painting, or creative process, was the reward. When Morris tried to end the painting session before Congo had exhausted his painting inclinations, the chimpanzee screamed and had temper tantrums. When a painting was finished, as far as Congo was concerned, he had no further interest in it and was ready to begin a new one. He made 384 drawings and paintings during the period of study.

The chimpanzee artist eventually shows a distinct awareness of designs and patterns. When marked sketch cards or papers were given the developing chimp artist it became obvious that the type and location of markings already on the paper influenced the chimpanzee's drawing. A circle and circular pattern formed of tiny squares was filled in by the chimp. A broken circle was bridged with scribbles and a triangle was bulwarked on each side with adjacent scribbles.

Small squares in the center of the paper were filled in with rough scribbles which overlapped the square's boundaries but were definitely centered on the square. One prepared pattern of three vertical bars was connected by several chimpanzee lines which hardly strayed from alignment.

A real surprise in chimpanzee art was the realization that chimpanzees have a good basic sense of composition and balance. Papers which had a square, or a vertical line well over to one side were handed the chimpanzee. The chimpanzee then confined his scribbles to the large open space opposite the prepared figure to achieve an obvious balance.

Although chimpanzees cannot make representations of objects from the human viewpoint it may be that they come relatively close to it from the chimpanzee viewpoint. A remarkable chalk drawing by the jungle-born Congo is

reproduced in Desmond Morris' book *The Biology of Art.*
The chimpanzee drew an egg-shaped "head." Several
marks inside it and on one side can be interpreted without
too much stretching as a nose, eye, and mouth. It is probably the most advanced art yet done by an ape.

Are chimpanzee paintings deliberate? At first, painting
is almost play because of the novelty, but photographs of
chimpanzees busy with their painting show complete
absorption in their work. Expressions change, mouths
twist and some chimps seem even to chew their tongues
as they create.

In addition to the art work of chimpanzees that of orangutans and capuchin monkeys has been studied. Neither,
however, exhibits the ability of the chimpanzee. This
may or may not mean that the chimpanzee is smarter, but
it does demonstrate better adaptation and possible motivation to an activity which man likes to consider exclusive
to himself.

Desmond Morris, who conducted the principal chimpanzee experiments, sent some test cards with various
diagrams on them to the Rotterdam Zoo. The gorilla
keeper supplied an adult female gorilla with them and
showed her how to use them. She worked with concentra-
tion and when the test cards were returned to Morris he
found that she had also positioned her scribbles in relation
to that of the various squares and lines.

This brings up the question of which is more intelligent,
gorilla or chimpanzee? Arthur Jones, perhaps today's
best known animal collector because of his television series
about his work, believes that the gorilla is the most intel-

ligent of the apes. Because of the gorilla's reserve and shyness, however, it gives the impression of being mentally inferior to the jungle extrovert, the chimpanzee.

The question of which is the smartest ape will remain unanswered for some time. Although basic investigations have been made on ape mentality, the subject has barely progressed beyond that step, especially in the case of the gorilla and baboon. Almost every new study of the chimpanzee, however, has uncovered unsuspected mental capacities.

There is no doubt that the chimpanzee puts the gorilla in the shade when it comes to making and using tools, at least in present habitats. The chimpanzee tends to live in habitats of changing seasonal food capacities. Periods of limited food supply have caused the chimpanzee to look for new food sources with the aid of simple tools. The gorilla has not been faced with this mental challenge. It has no need for tools when it can find adequate roots, shoots and leaves every day of the year in its present habitat. As a result, Dr. George Schaller believes the gorilla is now at an evolutionary mental dead end.

There is much to be learned about ape intelligence. What would happen if an orphaned gorilla were reared among chimpanzees and began imitating their tool uses? What would happen if a gorilla sanctuary were established on an island where normal food needs could only be met by gorillas doing the basic reasoning necessary to procure marginal food supplies? What would happen if an infant chimp were adopted by gorillas? Would it instinctively fashion tools to secure delicacies ignored by gorillas? Numberless other related questions have yet to be answered.

One of the most important discoveries made by Jane Goodall during her studies was that chimpanzees not only use tools but make tools, a situation which jarred a number of anthropologists who were schooled on the premise that a chief reason for man's dominance was that he was the only member of the animal kingdom able to make and use tools.

Chimpanzees make sponges. They chew a handful of leaves briefly to increase absorbency and dip this "sponge" into limb cracks and knots where water has collected too far down for their lips to reach. Testing this herself Jane found that the chewed leaves absorbed amounts up to eight times more than what could be licked from fingers. The chimpanzee dips such a sponge into the crack, allows it to fill with water, then lifts it out and sucks the liquid from it.

Jane watched chimps towel themselves clean with leaves after being soiled with mud, overripe bananas, with blood after a fight, or by infants.

She reported in her book *My Friends the Wild Chimpanzees* that her first really exciting observation occurred four months after her field work began. She paused to watch a chimp sitting by a termite nest.

He held a blade of sword grass in one hand and was carefully stripping away its sides. When little more than a stem remained he pushed it into a hole in the termite nest. He left it there for a moment before pulling it out and licking it. He did this repeatedly until the stem broke.

Then the chimp picked up a piece of vine, stripped the leaves off with one hand, bit off the end and used this to probe the holes he scratched through the surface with his index finger. Jane watched patiently until the chimp left, then stepped to the termite nest. Poking a grass blade into one of the holes she felt the worker termites bite it. When she pulled it out several termites were clinging to it. These were the delicacies for which the chimpanzee fished and ate.

After seeing many chimps use such tools, Jane wondered if chimps planned ahead their use, or was the tool use a result of convenience and more or less accidental?

She found that chimps occasionally selected stems for probing before they reached termite nests still out of sight. Once she saw a chimp pick up a grass stem and carry it for half a mile, visiting eight nests during the time but finding none of them worth probing.

One chimp on a termite fishing trip found that the only possible tools in the vicinity were clumps of dried grass some distance away from the termite hills. Several times the chimp went to the grass clumps and examined the stems carefully, selecting those best suited for his purpose. On each trip he selected about four and carried them along, tucking the spares into the space between thigh and abdomen or placing them on the ground beside him as he fished. Each stalk was broken into nine-inch probes before using and as it became frayed or bent he broke off the end or discarded it.

Only during certain periods are termite nests ripe for picking as far as chimpanzee fishing is concerned. This occurs when the rains begin and worker termites hollow passages almost to the surface. A thin layer of soil remains until the winged termites are ready to fly away and begin new colonies. The chimpanzees search for these thin seals of mud and the activity beneath them.

Once Jane watched an old male chimp push a three-foot stick into the underground nest of vicious safari ants. Leaving the stick in place he stepped back from the ants swarming out. A number climbed onto the chimp and he picked these off and ate them. Then he stepped back to the stick and pulled it out as Jane said, "with a magnificent gesture."

While standing upright he ate the massed ants off the stick and ignored those which bit him.

Christine, the chimp reared by Lilo Hess on her Pennsylvania farm, enjoyed pushing sticks into soft earth or moss. She gathered a handful of sticks, took them to a selected area and laid them by her side. Then she began pushing them into the ground, most often in a semi-circular fence. When they were all pushed in, she would rearrange them.

A stick served her as an arm extension whenever she played or explored near a stream or pond. She used the stick to poke the bottom in an attempt to alarm fish or frogs into movement.

When curious about the contents of a hollow log or hole in the ground Christine first explored it with a stick before placing her hand inside and raking out the dirt or leaves. She found sticks most useful otherwise for nest building. Although it is doubtful that she recalled seeing nest building during her first few weeks in her natural habitat, by the time she was five and Miss Hess took her on excursions into the Pennsylvania woods, Christine spent much time arranging dead sticks around herself as she sat upon the ground. Once the nest was built she lost interest in it. The next day, however, she might return to it and add sticks. She was selective in the type of sticks, discarding some and carrying desired ones from a distance of fifteen feet or farther. She never tried to build a nest among limbs. At home Christine often used her blanket and playthings to construct similar nests.

One of the most impressive uses of tools was that of a captive chimp who was provided with a two-foot-long pipe which had food lodged in its center. His only potential tool was a board of roughly the same length but three inches wide. The chimp soon had his food. He bit off a strip thin enough to insert into the pipe and dislodge the food.

Once a chimpanzee has watched a man use a key to open a lock he apparently never forgets this important information. Heinrich Oberjohann once kept chimps locked in an empty ship cabin during a trip from Africa to Europe. The chimps enjoyed wrestling with the man daily when he came to visit them. One day they piled on him and wrestled him to the floor. During the melee one chimp fished the key from his pocket, opened the door and raced out with the others at his heels.

Do chimpanzees use weapons? The answer is not clear. Excited chimpanzees throw rocks, chunks of earth, sticks, limbs and almost anything else within reach which can be thrown. Such throwing is generally wild but some chimpanzees have an ability to direct missiles at a target. Jane Goodall watched one chimpanzee hurl a stick much like a man throwing a spear. On another occasion she saw a chimpanzee hit a baboon twice out of three attempts. The baboon was only a yard away and the missiles—a pebble, a banana skin, and a handful of leaves—were insignificant, yet the results showed definite throwing ability.

Some chimp-thrown objects can be dangerous. Jane reported that one exuberant chimp hurled a large stone into the tent where her malaria-ridden husband lay. The stone missed his head by two inches. If it had hit his head, Jane said, it would have crushed his skull.

Recently I watched a film made by European scientists of chimpanzees attacking a stuffed leopard with sticks and limbs. As the men manipulated the leopard by pulling a cable the chimps rushed it, flung dirt at it and made hit-and-run attacks during which they pounded the stuffed leopard with sticks.

The throwing ability of apes improves remarkably when they are motivated to do so. Zoo chimpanzees have this motivation. Frustrated at the oppressive stares and presence of visitors they put on modified displays designed to drive them away. Desmond Morris told of chimps in

England's Chester Zoo tearing up clumps of sod and throwing them with "remarkable precision" across a water moat.

In a test of chimp ability to aim a thrown object, English zoologists set up an apparatus of sticks with grapes balanced on top of them. A tethered chimp was shown that if he swung a ball hung from a cord and knocked a stick down, a dislodged grape would roll within reach. Accuracy improved to near human capabilities after only a few trials.

The ability to handle and manipulate objects begins early for chimpanzees. Infants find temporary toys and spend hours playing with them. Two Gombe Stream Reserve infants were observed dragging "pull toys," one a dead mouse which the little chimp dragged by its tail and the other a twig with a berry cluster on its end. Another young chimp delighted in wild oranges, fruit of the *Strychnos* tree. It rested on its back, holding the fruit up with its hands while spinning it with its feet. Other young chimps flipped the oranges into the air to catch them in a hand or rested on their backs and rolled the oranges over their bodies. One young chimp played for some time with a cicada, holding the insect in its mouth by one wing while he listened to the insect's churring.

6: *Gorillas in the Wild*

THE FIRST MAN FROM THE MEDITERRANEAN AREA TO SEE A
gorilla was a Carthaginian Admiral named Hanno, who
sailed around to West Africa about 500 B. C. He told of
huge wild men called gorillas on the islands of West
Africa and adjacent mainland. Three skins of female
gorillas were brought to Carthage later, but the subject
seems to have been dropped for the next 2,300 years.

It was not until 1847 that the lowland gorilla was "discovered" by Savage and Wyman and facts about the animal were gathered. Early reports from Central African
explorers, including David Livingstone, told of contacts
with gorillas but subsequent data indicated some of these
were chimpanzees. In 1902 a German army officer,
Beringe, exploring the Virunga volcanoes along the Great
Rift Valley saw and shot two large apes. He had no previous knowledge of gorillas in the area and considered
that these animals might be chimpanzees of a previously
unknown size.

During the early 1900's various taxonomists, using
limited numbers of gorilla skulls, came up with numerous

"new" forms. However, gorillas are generally considered
at this writing to be divided into only two forms, or sub-
species. These are the *Gorilla gorilla gorilla*, or lowland
gorilla of West Africa's equatorial forests and the *Gorilla
gorilla beringei*, or mountain gorilla of Central Africa's
volcanic forests, chiefly west of the Rift Valley between
Lakes Edward and Tanganyika.

The mountain gorilla ranges into high, cold altitudes
which receive occasional snow. Tracks and droppings
have been seen at 12,000 and 12,400 feet on different vol-
canos and one naturalist, Gaston de Witte, found gorilla
droppings on the summit of Mount Visoke at 12,144 feet
altitude. In the Mikeno-Karisimbi area, 120 miles north
of Lake Tanganyika, the gorilla does not range below
8,500 feet, the lower limit of the forest which provides
its food.

The habitats of both gorillas are restricted to thick
forests where food plants thrive. Since gorillas do not
swim, or even wade large streams, rivers have served to
confine their natural ranges.

Both gorillas have arrived late on the stage viewed by
zoologists. Man has known very little about them until
very recently. A disastrous animal-collecting trip made
by Armand Denis resulted in thirty lowland gorilla cap-
tives procured about 200 miles north of Brazzaville in
what was then French Equatorial Africa (now the Congo
Republic). He made this trip during World War Two
when extraordinary difficulties were encountered in moving his valuable cargo. While waiting shipment to America, his gorillas began dying from an epidemic which

initially made them listless. Although every known treatment was tried, the gorillas slowly died, usually two days after contracting the disease. Autopsies eliminated all causes except for an unknown virus. Denis never learned the identity of the killer of his gorillas.

The first significant study of gorillas in their natural habitat was made in 1959–60 by an American scientist George B. Schaller who spent many months in the mountain gorilla's habitat of Central Africa. Schaller's principal method of collecting gorilla data from lengthy observation was simple. He put himself in full view of gorillas as quickly as possible so they could easily observe him and satisfy themselves that he offered no threat. Successful wildlife photographers and naturalists have used the technique successfully with such normally shy species as bighorn sheep which soon lose their suspicion when the observer tries to remain *in sight* instead of out of sight.

Although he occasionally observed from hiding, this method had limitations. When the gorillas moved and he attempted to follow, the chances were good that his movement and attempt to remain hidden would be spotted and the gorillas would flee the area.

Consequently, his favored tactic was to climb upon a stump or low limb as close as practicable to the gorillas where they could see him easily. After the initial pause at sighting him the chances were good that they would go about their normal routine and ignore him. Such gorillas soon accepted his presence and even approached him as close as five feet.

Schaller followed several rigid self-imposed rules. He

carried no weapon because he believed that possession of a firearm would give him an aggressiveness which he might not recognize but would be apparent to the gorillas. When they left an area he did not follow them so they would never feel pursued. He wore the same drab clothes so the gorillas could recognize him immediately. He usually approached gorillas alone, moving slowly and carrying no camera or binoculars initially until they were accustomed to his presence. As a consequence of these patient preparations he was able to study six groups over considerable periods.

He had no trouble recognizing groups and individuals. Gorilla faces are as distinctive as those of humans. Schaller even made diagrams of thirteen noses of gorillas belonging to one group. Each nose is readily distinguishable from the others at a glance. Body shapes, scars, postures and habits all contributed to easy recognition of groups.

He found that gorillas generally live in groups from two to thirty individuals with most in groups of six to twelve. When food is plentiful and the gorillas do not feel persecuted by man, the groups tend to be larger, a common situation with most gregarious species.

Although there is much to learn about the factors which decide the numbers in a group it seems that the average group of six to twelve gorillas is more stable than a small group with limited contact with other gorillas, or a large group which cannot move easily through the jungle without losing some of its members.

What causes a group of gorillas to form? Each group usually has a dominant male, most often a silverbacked male in its prime. Groups form casually, not as a result of a furious fight between competing males. Large groups break into parts during feeding, travel or nesting and these parts may separate themselves from the main group to begin a new group. Occasionally a lone male joins a group and one or more females may wander away with him, thus forming a new group.

In any group, the leader is almost always the largest silverbacked male. He is dominant over all including the other silverbacks. These in turn dominate all blackbacked —younger adult—males and females. These young male adults and adult females dominate all juveniles and infants not carried by their mothers. Although there is an order of rank among the adult males within their age groups, there is none among the adult females.

One of the surprises the gorilla has for most of us is its peaceful, placid temperament. Gorillas show few scars from fighting with each other. Strange gorillas wander out of the vegetation, feed with the group for a few minutes or a few weeks and if he shows no indication of disputing the dominant male's authority, he is largely ignored. Different groups meet and mingle casually without argument, then go their separate ways. Irritations by subordinate members of the group usually bring nothing more than a hard look or a bluffing demonstration which commonly stops the cause of irritation. The group's leader may entirely ignore a strange male wandering out of the foliage to mate with a female near him, yet the slightest threat to his group arouses him immediately.

This quick anger has its desired effect on intruding men.

The first non-Africans to bring back stories of irritated gorillas told vivid stories of intimidation which immediately cloaked the gorilla with an aura of ferocity it has never shed. Most of us were reared on a picture of the gorilla as a screaming, chest-beating, demon who snapped rifles as if they were dry sticks.

The less we know about an animal species the more inclined we are to assign briefly observed behavior as that which can be expected of all individuals of the species. Most flagrant of these violations of objective observation seems to be the statement often made by scientists and naturalists—that a particular species does not attack man. Most of us would not consider dogs dangerous to man—certainly not animals which would attack man with the ferocity of wild beasts—yet there are probably more attacks, or at least bites, of man by dogs throughout the world each day than by all other animal species.

Does the gorilla attack man? Typically, most adult gorillas attempt to send man on his way with a display which resembles a charge. Usually the charge stops a few feet away if the man shows no indication of retreat, and the gorilla turns away to disappear.

There is one almost certain way to invite physical attack by a charging gorilla or by the neighbor's barking dog. That is to turn and run. One hunter collecting museum specimens in the Congo reported that a gorilla group leader charged him seven different times but usually stopped short of exposing himself to the man's sight. The hunter held his ground each time.

The same hunter reported the case of a badly scarred

native who survived a gorilla attack. The native was hunting monkeys with a crossbow—an unusual weapon in equatorial Africa—when he was confronted in the thick brush by a large male gorilla. The gorilla charged, stopped and moved off a short distance. When it charged again the native's nerve failed him and he turned to run. The gorilla's hand missed his hips but seized an ankle. The native fought off the gorilla, using the crossbow as a club. Two more attacks were repelled by hand-to-hand fighting before it left. The man was severely bitten, however.

This report is not particularly rare. Many natives of today's gorilla habitat can show scars of gorilla contact, but far more natives of gorilla habitat can show scars left by domestic dog teeth.

Leopards seem to be the only predator, other than man, presenting a danger to the gorilla in its natural habitat. This danger is limited, however. Authentic records exist of leopards killing adult males and females but such cases are rare. Since defenseless animals such as duikers—small antelopes—and hyraxes abound in the mountain gorilla's habitat, these are the leopard's common food. Apparently a rare leopard develops a taste for the gorilla just as a rare leopard becomes a man-killer.

For some reason large birds flying overhead startle gorillas while large potentially dangerous animals such as elephants and buffalo are ignored even though they may be only a few yards away. Zoo gorillas in the vicinity of airports also react to aircraft flying overhead, stopping play or other activity to look up.

The experienced African tracker knows much about the

anxiety and mental condition of the animal he follows by observing the consistency of digestive wastes. An elephant tracker spotting almost liquid wastes knows there is little point in attempting to catch the elephants because they are nervous and fully aware of pursuit. They move fast with few if any pauses.

Schaller's extended gorilla observations confirmed that their seemingly placid nature was typical in the wild. They were not easily excited and when he followed spoor of a group to a point where he could observe them only once did he see evidence of an excited gorilla as shown by this indicator. This occurred when he persisted in following the track of a young male adult traveling alone. Successive thinner droppings showed the gorilla's apprehension.

Despite the tales of gorilla ferocity, early hunters found that the gorilla offered little danger to them. Before the creation of the gorilla sanctuaries the much persecuted gorilla showed none of the dangerous retaliatory tactics of the elephant, lion or leopard. When Carl Akeley hunted specimens for museum collections, his native guides were content to point out gorilla locations, then sit down so he could fire over their heads. None of them would dare do this, however, when hunting elephants. After the elephant was located and pointed out the guides immediately moved to safer places far behind the hunter.

Practically nothing is known about gorilla behavior toward man in the centuries before Europeans came with their more effective weapons. Most species of wildlife which once dominated certain habitats had limited respect toward early man and his primitive weapons. However, the coming of the rifle brought a marked change. Lions and elephants hunted by rifles became secretive and avoided man if at all possible.

The gorilla of two centuries ago may have been a terror to African natives. He is not now, and it is doubtful that the gorilla ever was the jungle terror which some fiction writers have depicted. The gorilla has always lived in a habitat of ample vegetation which provided its food. It probably never had a real motivation to be anything other than a peaceful vegetarian.

The average gorilla goes to considerable effort to stay out of man's way, except when stimulated by the proximity of a rich field of sugar cane or bananas. In 1926, Mary Akeley said that a group of twenty-two gorillas slept regularly each night a few rods from her camp. Large beds of wild celery had attracted them to the spot. They were so quiet that she never heard them although she lay awake late each night in an attempt to catch any sound.

Do gorillas beat their chests? Yes, they do, quite freely when they feel like it. The drumming is not an isolated act but is part of a display consisting of nine separate steps. After months of observing gorillas, George Schaller listed these and found that the complete display included all of the acts. Occasionally the display ended abruptly at any stage.

The first act in this ritual is hooting which begins slowly, accelerates, and merges into a single sound. Symbolic feeding occurs next when the gorilla snatches a leaf or stalk and places it between his lips. Then the gorilla stands erect, sometimes simultaneously scooping up a handful of vegetation to fling into the air, or he may do this a moment later.

Now the chest-beating begins. The alternate hand slaps are furiously fast and the gorilla may kick out with one leg. Now the gorilla runs a few steps to one side, then recklessly slaps and tears limbs and vines out of his way. The last act in this ritual is one hard thump of the ground with his open hand.

Schaller reported that gorillas giving this chest-beating display often stopped and looked to see what effect the display had on him. Younger gorillas often sat down after beating chests, or abdomens, thighs, nearby logs or even the tops of their heads, and looked around to see what effect this had on their companions.

The most dangerous part of the display comes when the gorilla begins tearing up vegetation. If one of his own group is within reach the gorilla may be struck. Men, at which the display is directed, may be struck even though they have shown no indication of intimidation. The display, or "charge," usually ends a few feet away when the gorilla suddenly loses its belligerence and flees. Some men have been struck by a furious gorilla, however, as they faced it. It is almost certain that a gorilla observer invites disaster if he turns to run at this critical moment.

To gorillas, as well as most apes and monkeys, a glare means belligerence and none do more than glance at a companion because of this. To show appeasement or friendliness an ape or monkey turns its head aside. If it desires to show submission to a staring companion it shakes its head. The warmest handshake I ever received came from a large spider monkey in lower Mexico when it reached out to grasp my extended forefinger and wrapped its four fingers around it. Then it looked aside and down in the "courteous" manner of its kind.

Gorilla belligerence toward other gorillas intensifies after a stare if the gorilla lunges slightly to suggest a charge about to be launched. A bluffing charge may be silent or roaring, but if the aggressive gorilla is highly agitated it may seize its opponent to wrestle and bite.

The gorilla leader's role is similar to that of most gregarious wildlife species. When he is ready to travel he sets off with determination which is sensed almost immediately by all members of the group, and they stop their activity to follow. He may or may not grunt to gain attention.

Armand Denis often heard and saw gorilla handclapping in West Africa during which the hands were slightly cupped. The action reminded Denis of the way the early African colonials summoned servants and he believed it to be used primarily as an assembly call by a dominant male to summon members of his group. During animal collection hunts in which many natives participated, Denis often heard the clapping signals.

The leader is the guardian of the group as well. If a rear-guard display is deemed necessary he takes care of it. At night he is the first to begin building a nest. As soon as the group members see that he is serious they build their own.

Schaller has never observed gorillas using tools. This

does not indicate a lack of capacity to do so, however, since gorillas live in habitats where food is so easily obtained that there is never need for tools. He did observe a makeshift bridge of several tree ferns bent into an eight-foot-wide stream to provide better footing for crossing. This approaches tool-using in the conventional use of the term. Young gorillas under the care of a human foster father are eager to imitate his actions and gorillas quickly learn the use of eating utensils.

Gorillas do throw things as many zoo visitors have found. Caged gorillas irritated by noisy crowds pick up any small object—scraps of food or wastes—and throw it through the bars with adequate accuracy.

According to one way of thinking, nest building is akin to tool use, that is, the changing or improving of the environment to satisfy the builder's need. Gorillas are more enthusiastic nest builders than chimpanzees and they construct them rapidly for day naps or for sleeping at night. They may be on the ground, in a tree or a few feet high in a bamboo thicket. Although construction is generally simple with the gorilla standing in one place and pulling limbs and stalks toward his chosen site, occasionally a nest indicates some comprehension of a need for interlocking limbs.

More nests are built on the ground than above it and the large adults tend to build entirely on the ground. Young gorillas and females with infants build tree nests which are primarily platforms to prevent a fall during the night. Ground nests built on steep hillsides seem to be designed to prevent sliding or rolling while sleeping. The purpose of the average ground nest is not easily ascertained. Usually it consists of no more than a rim of bent or broken vegetation with almost nothing in the nest's bottom to insulate the user from cold or for comfort. It may be an instinctive carry-over from a more active life in the trees while young.

Night nesting places seldom cover an area larger than a half acre and are arranged casually. The dominant silverbacked male may be near the center of the group or at the edge, as are the females with infants. The nests apparently are never used on consecutive nights, although an occasional return visit may cause them to use some of the nests again.

The nest area does not represent territorial claim since gorillas are nomadic with no interest in establishing a claimed area to be defended against encroachment. During the day they may wander no more than a hundred yards, or they may go as much as three miles. The nesting area, if at all suitable, is dictated by where feeding ends.

The home range of mountain gorillas probably averages from ten to fifteen square miles and may be used by as many as a half dozen groups at one time. Chance meetings or minglings by two groups usually cause no friction and the groups largely ignore each other. No instances have been reported of gorillas showing any of the territorial instincts which are so strong in many species that they cause a spirited defense. Males show no possessive jealousy when other males have interest in females, or mate with them. Chances are good that they wander away eating.

Gorillas are strictly day "people." They do not get out

of their nests until daybreak and go to bed promptly at nightfall. During the day they have definite patterns of activity which vary in length and are influenced by the weather, but are still routine. They feed soon after arising until mid-morning and rest or nap until about two in the afternoon. A few may make quick nests for their naps. Then they move about eating, or just wander about if not hungry. By five in the afternoon activity draws to a close and preparations for the night begin.

Schaller found no instances of night movement during his observations. He heard no snoring although he did hear an occasional burst of chest beating when other groups or lone males were in the vicinity.

The night nesting area is located in various places: jungled valleys, slopes, or within a few hundred feet of villages or camps. In areas frequented by both chimpanzees and gorillas, the chimpanzee nests tend to be much higher than those of the gorillas. Gorillas seldom build nests more than ten feet off the ground while chimpanzee nests have been recorded at heights of 140 feet.

Schaller found many mountain gorilla nesting areas with one or more unused nests. He believed these were made by juvenile gorillas as soon as the silverback leader began constructing his. As the group fed on past the silverback before nest building, the juvenile decided to build another close to the main group.

Gorillas love to sunbathe. Contrary to the picture much gorilla literature gives us, the gorillas are not partial to the darkest jungle. Such jungles are usually climax forests with foliage canopies thick enough to prevent the sun's

rays from reaching the ground and thus stimulating under-story, or brush growth, which contains the principal food plants. Consequently, gorillas are most often found in secondary forests where the sun stimulates vegetation at ground level.

When the sun breaks through the clouds, observers have watched gorillas stop activity immediately and stretch out, even spread-eagle, on their backs to expose chests and stomachs to the warm rays. Schaller watched gorillas sunbathe like this for two hours at a time until sweat trickled down faces and chests.

They pay little attention to light rains and often sit out in heavy rains. Their response to rain varies, however, since gorillas may seek shelter under trees or overhanging rocks. Rain seems to be as depressing to gorillas as to humans in similar circumstances. They huddle and pay little attention to movement or noise around them. By accident, Schaller walked through a group of huddling, soaked gorillas one day and only one bothered to look up.

Streams are major barriers to gorillas, even shallow streams which block retreat from hunting natives. If there are no fallen trees bridging a jungle stream too wide to leap across, gorillas turn aside.

It is only natural to assume that the gorilla, born and reared in the jungle, has a dexterity and sense of balance which protect him from accidents that would cause man much discomfort in this habitat. Actually this is not a true picture. Gorillas stumble or fall and break arms, legs, ribs and other bones. They rush through thick brush, tearing themselves on thorns and puncturing themselves with broken limbs. They show notoriously poor judgment of the capacity of a limb to support them and step on or hang from limbs which come crashing down. This situation is relatively frequent according to observers who have watched them most in the jungles.

All things considered, could a man show more agility on the rough ground and trees of the gorilla's habitat than a gorilla? Yes, it is possible that he could, especially in tree limbs where the gorilla's bulk becomes a disadvantage. Gorilla arms are superior to man's but gorilla legs are much inferior. No adult gorilla could match a human gymnast.

In a tree, the gorilla moves generally on all fours and does little or no hand-over-hand movement while hanging beneath a limb. Jumping among limbs is rare and when descending, he climbs down in an upright position facing the trunk.

Most of the gorilla's time is spent on the ground. About one-third of its day is spent sitting in an upright position as it feeds and grooms itself. At times a gorilla may walk several steps in an upright position and gorillas breaking into flight often take the first few steps erect before falling forward onto all fours which is their typical posture for movement.

Like the chimpanzee, the gorilla walks on the knuckles of its hands, or forefeet, and on the soles or sides of its rear feet. The spread of a gorilla's arms is amazing. The spread of one killed by Carl Akeley at Karisimbi near Lake Kivu measured over eight feet, actually ninety-seven inches.

Among the lesser physical features which remind man

of his distant kinship with the gorilla are fingernails. This brings up a question. How do gorillas and chimps keep their fingernails trimmed? Like hoofed animals, normal wear performs the function adequately. A wild horse living on soft soil containing little grit is soon in difficulty from overgrown hoofs. When the horse has access to the usual rocky, gritty or sandy soil hoof growth is worn away as fast as it grows. Similarly chimpanzees and gorillas use their hands and feet against rough surfaces—wood, rocks and gritty soil—enough to keep nails short.

What is the gorilla's principal sense? As in man, sight seems to be the most important and depended-upon sense. Yet Schaller's extended observations convinced him that the gorilla's seemingly uncanny sight is no more acute than that of man. Schaller found that as soon as he grew accustomed to gorilla habitat, any sound, smell or movement which caught the gorilla's attention also caught his own attention just as quickly.

He soon found that he had to take no special precautions against natural sounds when approaching a gorilla group. If he stepped on a stick the gorillas paid no attention since the noise was no different than that made by a gorilla breaking a stick. An unnatural noise brought heads up, and no sound was as alarming as a human voice. Invariably this sent the gorillas fleeing in silence.

It seems almost a paradox that the shy gorilla prefers to live near man. When natives abandon fields for new ones, gorillas tend to move within feeding distance of these overgrown fields. A new road through the jungle with its border of spreading small farms and villages with clearings around them, actually draws gorillas to it rather than sends them deeper into the jungle. Villages abandoned after several years are often visited regularly by feeding gorilla groups. This situation causes the colonization of some new areas by gorillas and may be a boon to the overall gorilla population.

The real danger to some mountain gorilla groups, however, is the steady erosion of jungle which is never returned to the wild. Small farms and pastures eat away the edges of the mountain forests and never allow gorilla food plants to reestablish themselves so that some gorilla habitat is shrinking.

The mountain gorilla's original habitat has been cultivated in a sense by elephant herds, fires and storms which open the jungle and allow the sun to penetrate and stimulate the growth of wild celery beds and other gorilla foods.

Fortunately, conservation of the mountain gorilla began early. In 1925 when the Congo belonged to Belgium King Albert decreed that the present Albert Park would be a gorilla sanctuary set aside for purely scientific purposes. This meant that only a very few scientists would be permitted to visit the park for unobtrusive study.

A strange attitude toward gorillas is still held by at least one tribe in former French Equatorial Africa (now Congo Republic). Armand Denis visited the tribe's village, Oka, in the early 1940's and found that the village's life was based on the gorilla. They were at war literally with nearby gorillas. They killed them not only for food but recklessly at every opportunity as if the gorilla groups were dangerous and competing tribes.

Before a gorilla hunt the tribe held the traditional war dances the night before while trackers located sleeping gorillas. Before dawn some 400 villagers arrived with nets, spears and guns, and erected the net into a five-foot-high fence around the sleeping gorillas. The next morning when the dominant male charged the net, followed by other gorillas, a rain of spears and bullets began. Any extra large male gorilla slain generated much excitement since the villagers considered him an important tribal leader.

How many gorillas live in Africa today? Estimates vary widely. The lowland gorilla populations are scattered over an area which has been subject to little wildlife study. However, it is generally recognized that the lowland gorilla is more numerous than the mountain gorilla. Desmond Morris recently estimated about 60,000 lowland gorillas alive today in central West Africa and between 5,000 and 15,000 mountain gorillas in Central Africa's high country. A survey of the mountain gorilla's distribution over a six-month period by Emlen and Schaller suggested a 1960 figure of 3,000 to 15,000.

Other than spots of encroaching agriculture there seems to be nothing on the immediate horizon to endanger Africa's principal gorilla population and habitats. Over-all the population seems to be stable. The meat hunting by natives which is done today is less than that of the past due to game regulations and sport hunting has been strictly controlled for many years. There are many areas where gorilla populations are definitely growing. One Uganda Game Department estimate of 1949 suggested that gorillas in its Kayonza Forest had increased by half over the previous twenty years.

The gorilla has played a vital part in opening the door to Africa for outsiders. It was a gorilla that never lived, but existed only in the mind of such people as Edgar Rice Burroughs who began one of the world's most successful book series with his *Tarzan of the Apes*. Burroughs could stimulate the reader's quest for adventure as few people could and his gorillas could do things real gorillas never did, swinging through tree limbs with the agility of monkeys and carrying on extended conversations which included future events. His jungles included lions and tigers until later research corrected these misplaced animals and eventually made Burroughs an authority on African natural history. But the gorilla remained an essential ingredient to the Tarzan books and this huge man-like animal captured the imaginations of school-boy readers throughout the world by saying in effect, if not literally, "Come, and see Africa. It is filled with strange animals and adventures like no other place."

7: *Gorilla Family Life*

THE MOST IMPORTANT INSIGHT INTO GORILLA MOTHER-infant relationships began with the birth of "Jambo" in the Basel, Switzerland Zoo. Jambo is the Swahili (East African) word for "Good Day." It was a good day for gorillas in general as well as zoo men over the world.

Although two other gorilla infants had been born in zoos, neither was reared by its mother. Jambo did live with his mother and zoo directors learned that it was possible at last to rear a zoo-born gorilla in a natural family situation.

The difficulty with the first two births was that neither mother knew how to rear her offspring. The first infant, "Colo," was born in the Columbus, Ohio Zoo in December, 1956. The mother abandoned her immediately. A zoo keeper found the infant on the cold floor and quick action by the zoo staff revived Colo. Under careful rearing by the zoo staff she soon became a healthy young gorilla and within a half dozen years weighed 130 pounds.

The second zoo birth was Goma, also born at the Basel Zoo in 1959. Goma's mother was Achilla, a huge lowland gorilla twelve years old. However, Achilla did not know how to feed her young one. She held it gently to her breast but with its face turned away and the infant could not nurse.

Jambo was born nineteen months later and anxious zoo men watched Achilla hold her new arrival with its face turned away from her chest during the first day. She was obviously proud of her four-pound offspring and held it out for chimpanzees in an adjacent cage to see as well as to zoo staff members.

On the second day apprehensions were dispelled. Jambo nursed hungrily and feeding continued normally. When Jambo grew a bit Achilla tried to feed it soup with a spoon as she had learned to do. This was unsuccessful, however.

Gorilla newborn do not have the tenacious grip of the infant chimpanzee and cannot seize a handful of hair when the mother sets it down. After holding him continually for his first five days, Achilla set Jambo on the floor, but he began a loud protest and she picked him up again. After a number of repetitions, however, she was able to set him down without his crying. No other anthropoid mother can set her infant down at such an early age because of the infant's grip.

When Jambo was three months old zoo attendants watched Achilla place him on the floor and back away to induce him to crawl. Six weeks later Jambo could propel himself up on all fours in an attempt to walk like his mother and within another two weeks was doing an acceptable job of it.

Teething began at two months and Jambo tried to eat fruit and zoo foods prepared for his mother, but he continued to nurse until about eighteen months old. He was given milk now from a pitcher and by two years was completely weaned.

The zoo staff soon placed a three-year-old female in an adjacent cage and the two youngsters got to know each other through the wire. Then one day Jambo was admitted to her cage and the two embraced each other happily. There were no problems and the two playful youngsters were reared together. Shortly Achilla was reunited with her mate and after two weeks of occasional spats the two oldsters settled down again to a calm existence. Other zoos have had successful births since then. By 1966, there had been seven.

Gorillas are generally considered infants up to the age of three years and during this period they ride on their mothers' backs for long periods. The three-to-six year old weighs sixty and 120 pounds and is considered a juvenile by zoologists. A female of six is an adult, however, a male is considered a young adult until the age of ten and is usually blackbacked. The silverbacked male acquires the coloration which distinguishes it at about ten years and reaches its largest weight, often over 300 pounds and occasionally, over 400. One mountain gorilla in the San Diego Zoo weighed well over 600 pounds before death. Like virtually all species gorillas accumulate weights in zoos which they do not acquire in the wild. One of the largest wild gorillas taken was a 482-pound mountain gorilla killed by Commander Gatti in 1936. It was six feet nine inches high.

Females while giving birth to young do not drop out of the group. The new offspring is so small that a casual observer would not notice it. The infant is helpless for the first few weeks of its life when it nurses for long periods and is incapable of any independent movement. Soon after reaching the age of two months it begins to nibble on plant foods and by the age of eight months most of its food is plant life.

Infant gorillas develop twice as fast as human babies and significantly faster than the smaller chimpanzee. Accurate data have been impractical to get by jungle observations but there is reason to believe that free-living gorilla infants do progress faster than zoo-born infants.

Infant gorillas can crawl by pushing themselves with their feet at less than three months. Chimpanzee infants take a week or so longer and human babies three times as long, or generally about nine months. A gorilla can stand erect at about four months, a chimp at about six months and a human baby at about eight months. Wild gorilla infants can move along nicely on all fours in the typical gorilla gait at four months, two months earlier than zoo-born gorilla infants.

In the jungle, the little gorilla begins to play with other infants at four months and to climb without its mother's help. By six months, gorilla infants are exuberant youngsters with good control of their arms and legs. They climb into bushes and swing from low limbs and trailing vines.

Running and wrestling take up much of their play time after the gorilla group's morning feeding period.

Wrestling often takes the form of a ritual similar to that of Japanese wrestlers. Two little gorillas stand erect and slowly, perhaps unsteadily, walk toward each other. When they contact, the grappling seems like that on slow-motion film. As many as three gorilla infants have been observed doing a snake dance by aligning themselves and with hands on the hips of the one in front, move along like a disjointed snake. Games of tag and goat-on-the-mountain begin spontaneously at this age.

If no playmates are around, the little gorilla may turn somersaults to occupy himself. A bunch of leaves or moss serves as something to swing about and may end on top the infant's head as a makeshift hat. One infant placed moss on its head like a cap and walked along a limb holding its head steady to prevent dislodging the moss.

Infants often imitate their elders in play. Schaller watched one youngster run stiff-legged along a log, rise unsteadily to its feet, and beat its chest with exaggerated motions.

Such play is limited, however, in comparison to that of chimpanzee youngsters. The gorilla never seems to have the chimp's exuberance at any age. Weather is also a factor, especially in mountain gorilla habitat where low clouds and heavy overcasts have the same depressing effects on gorillas as upon humans.

Older gorillas, juveniles and adults are tolerant toward infants. The gruffest old silverbacked male is not apt to show any irritability when a youngster crawls over him

or goes to sleep against him. He may even give a grand-fatherly swat to a passing infant. An excited male rushing recklessly toward an infant may be stopped abruptly by the infant's whimper.

The dominant male attracts infants in much the same way a grandfather does. When the group is resting several infants may leave their mothers to crowd around him. They slap his face, sit in his lap and even hitch rides by hanging onto his rump hairs without wearing out their welcome.

Gorilla populations do not expand rapidly. A female produces an offspring about once every four years so that her lifetime production is four or five. This number may increase if the infants die early and she breeds again soon thereafter. Disease kills more gorillas than poachers and natural predators, such as the leopard. Many of man's afflictions affect the gorilla. Arthritis had crippled fifteen of eighty-nine gorillas whose skeletons were examined by one investigator. The death rate is highest during a gorilla's first year and almost half of the young gorillas die within the first six years. Those surviving youth are apt to live to a ripe old age which is believed to be about twenty years for wild gorillas. One male in the Phila-delphia Zoo, however, reached an age of thirty-four years and one-half.

Few people are willing to admit that the gorilla is far ahead of *Homo sapiens* in some matters. However, if there is one thing that is significantly ahead of human behavior it is in offspring discipline. All of us know parents whose ignorance of child discipline and guidance is appalling.

We can watch and hear parents in their homes, in the supermarket, in church and every public place screaming at their offspring, punishing them repeatedly, or going to the other extreme of allowing so much permissiveness that the child is uncontrollable.

Gorilla parents need only to direct a quiet stare at an unruly youngster to bring quick correction of misbehavior. Schaller, during his many months of gorilla observations, watched two infants play on the group's dominant silverback male. One shoved the other off. Then both wrestled over the old ape's legs until he had had enough. The silverback finally turned and gave them a "calm stare." One infant left. The other sat down immediately.

Schaller watched a gorilla mother sitting with her one-year-old near her leg. When she was ready to move she tapped it on the back with her fingers and immediately it climbed onto her back. Almost all control measures by adults were in this low key, even when a mother weaned a persistent youngster. She merely pushed it away, gently but firmly, and this usually conveyed the message.

Gorilla infants get off to a secure start in life because of their continuous body contact with their mothers. An infant never loses this security during its early days and it is constantly aware of its mother's firmness, as well as protectiveness. Thus, there is no need for such severe punishments as the wild cuffs which the mother bear administers to her cubs.

Then, am I saying the mother gorilla does a better job of rearing her offspring than many human mothers? Yes, I am suggesting exactly that.

If we could learn from gorilla behavior, could we also learn from the chimpanzee? Since frustration and anger in the chimpanzee take the form of screams, flapping arms and throwing things, it appears that chimpanzees have no real innovations to offer us in this department. *Homo sapiens* is already adept at this behavior.

8: *How Smart?*

THE MORE WE LEARN ABOUT APES AND OTHER ANIMALS THE faster we discard old concepts about animal intelligence. For too long man has insisted that animals cannot plan and reason, cannot make and use tools, and cannot appreciate the esthetic qualities of its environment. Now it is obvious that a great many animals can do all these things in varying degrees, if not in man's manner, certainly in that animal's manner.

Is the chimpanzee at all human? The zoologist is still inclined to answer this with one word, "Ridiculous!" The person who has known the chimpanzee in its own habitat the longest hedges his answer cautiously, however. In many circumstances the line between human and chimpanzee behavior becomes fuzzy.

Chimpanzees have been used many times by Africans and others to do housework, even housework requiring something more than action by rote. In such situations, the chimps identify with the humans who adopt them and model all practical actions after their human benefactor.

A chimpanzee is even intelligent enough to recognize

its dominance over natives of its African habitat when that occurs and does not hesitate to play the part of a tyrant, lording it over unarmed natives at every opportunity.

Heinrich Oberjohann discovered an old African living in the jungle with a chimpanzee which the man had rescued as an infant and reared. The chimpanzee brought water to the old man when asked and did other such tasks. Oberjohann, as a favor to the old man, invited him to his camp as a "keeper." The four-year-old chimp walked at the enfeebled old man's side, the ape erect as a young athlete, holding his benefactor's hand to furnish support and carrying the old man's possessions in a bag slung over his shoulder.

After some harrowing incidents between the chimp and camp workers when the chimp tried to continue his daily chores, such as taking water buckets from the kitchen, the chimpanzee settled into an acceptable routine. He carried wood and water for the cook and performed well as a kitchen boy. Unfortunately, he made a pest of himself whenever his enthusiastic imitations, such as taking over the camp clothes washing from a boy, resulted in misdirected effort. The chimp performed every act, soaping, scrubbing, rinsing, wringing, but then threw the clean clothes into the grass.

Perhaps the most amazing example of this chimp's mental capacity happened one afternoon when a camp boy went to get water. The chimp approached Oberjohann for a bucket to do the same. After some argument, the latter finally gave him an old bucket but punched several holes in the bottom to discourage this activity. The chimp grumbled as he took the bucket and headed for the river.

When the boy returned with his water Oberjohann asked what had happened to the chimp. The boy said he disappeared into the jungle. In another half hour the chimpanzee came into sight, carrying the bucket clasped against his chest. Every few steps he set the heavy bucket down, and rested because the process of carrying the weight in an upright position was exhausting.

When the chimpanzee passed, Oberjohann saw to his amazement that the bucket was full of water. After the chimpanzee emptied the water, Oberjohann examined the pail. Each hole had been closed by wooden splinters.

For too long we have tried to measure animal intellect with tests devised for measuring human intellect, tests which have a relation to man's environment and habitat but little or no relation to an animal's. Still the chimpanzee has shown a remarkable ability to step into man's world and learn skills which have no relation to its natural environment. One chimpanzee at New Mexico's Holloman Air Force Base, where space experimentation is conducted, learned to play tic-tac-toe on an electronic board so well that it frequently beat the experimenter.

In 1941, Armand Denis established a chimpanzee farm near Miami, Florida, intending to provide chimpanzees for research purposes. Since chimps have a relative immunity to such diseases as malaria and cancer, he felt that a station which could provide a number of healthy chimps could make an important contribution to medical science. At the same time he would admit paying visitors.

The chimps were given unusual freedoms. Instead of being caged in small enclosures or thrown together in larger enclosures and larger groups where bullying and fighting were apt to happen, Denis' chimps were held by long chains affixed to neck collars. Each chain was long enough to allow the chimp to play with an adjacent chimp if he wanted to, and if he did not the chimp could move closer to the tree anchoring his chain and have privacy. It was an unique and humane arrangement.

Although the station had a limited time of operation before World War Two Denis learned as much from the chimps as did the scientists. Most impressive to him was the vast difference in chimp personalities. Most impressive to readers of his book *On Safari* was the amazing exploits of a female he called Katie. She was a lock picker without equal.

Many of the chimpanzees soon learned the technique of opening the padlocks on their chains with a piece of bent wire after watching keepers open the locks with keys. However, most of Denis' chimps with lock-picking abilities had a frustration level. When they reached this they threw down the wires and had a temper tantrum. After they had calmed down they began again as if nothing had happened. Katie never had these tantrums. She could work patiently as long as necessary to make the lock snap open. As a consequence special efforts were made to insure that no piece of wire or hairpin was left within reach.

Denis said that before long she had to be padlocked in a cage at night and this was also padlocked. Even so on several occasions she picked both locks during the night and escaped temporarily.

One morning Denis learned that Katie had picked up another trick which she was using to her advantage. This was the use of bananas as rewards for doing certain tasks. At the chimp farm Denis had trained the chimps to clean their own night cages by giving bananas as rewards. The chimps loved it. As soon as they saw Denis coming with a stalk of bananas debris rained through the bars.

On this particular day Denis' attention was attracted to a number of laughing people gathered near Katie. Approaching, Denis saw Katie holding out a banana with one hand and pointing to a piece of wire on the ground beyond her reach. Finally one visitor pushed the wire to her.

Instead of rewarding him with the banana as she had indicated, she quickly turned her back and ate it. Taking the straight wire she bunched her chain on the ground, laid the wire on it and used another section of the slack chain to beat the end into a right angle.

Denis began timing her as she set to work with her lock picker. The lock snapped open in twelve minutes.

Apes have a comparatively larger brain at birth than human babies. A young ape is "smarter" than a human baby at birth and develops roughly twice as fast for the first three years.

Why is the human baby relatively retarded mentally— and these are figurative rather than literal terms—at birth compared to apes? Early in the evolutionary process which produced modern man, as the human brain developed in size, the conflict of a large baby head and the mother's constricted birth channel had to be resolved. The result was a relatively small brain at birth—less than one-fourth the size of an adult's—and significant growth later. The apes do not have anywhere near this potential for brain development after birth. A chimpanzee's brain reaches its maximum growth within twelve months after birth. A man's brain continues to grow into adult life.

It appears that mental limitations prevent the chimpanzee from speaking man's words. Their physical equipment, tongue, larynx and jaw, seems adequate for pronunciation and although many young chimpanzees in man's environment try to produce words through imitation, they seldom achieve even one word.

Heinrich Oberjohann has found three vowels—a, o and u—in chimpanzee talk. These are usually preceded by an "h" sound. Chimpanzees unite these sounds to form the words or combination of sounds which convey meaning. Pitch and tonal gradations refine the sounds and their meanings.

Some sounds or exclamations cover many situations just as do human exclamations. The sound "ho" given twice may express satisfaction, or it may indicate surprise.

A series of "ha-ha" sounds lifts chimpanzee ears within hearing because it tells of rising irritability. Other sounds may follow, pitched high and low alternately. A man associated with chimpanzees over a period of time can usually detect the reason for such sounds before he actually sees the cause. If the "ha! ha!" is heard from two chimps there is little doubt that a challenge has been accepted and a fight or at least a vigorous tongue-lashing is in prospect.

The most successful efforts to date toward teaching chimps to imitate and understand human words have been made by Dr. Keith Hayes and his wife Cathy. They reared a chimpanzee infant called "Viki" as they would a child. By the age of three, Viki could make acceptable imitations of three words, "Mama," "Papa," and "Cup." She had some understanding of their meaning and eventually learned to whisper "cup" when she wanted a drink.

By the age of six, Viki could produce seven acceptable words, not a very satisfactory accomplishment in comparison to children who may use hundreds of useful words at two.

Apparently chimpanzees can learn a number of word meanings although the extent of this has yet to be fully measured. Christine, the infant chimp reared in a home in a child's environment, enjoyed looking at pictures in books and magazines. Her foster parent occasionally showed her photos of apes in a background of other objects and asked, "Where is Christine?" The little chimp would point to the chimp in the photo for perhaps half a dozen times then point to some other object. Her foster parent, Lilo Hess, reported that there was no indication as to whether she grew tired of answering correctly, or did not know the difference.

An interesting query into the level of chimp learning was provided by a set of children's wooden blocks with outline pictures of animals. Miss Hess set up the blocks with only one familiar animal showing among several unfamiliar ones. Then she asked Christine to indicate the chicken, or horse, or cat. She always pointed to the correct one under such circumstances.

The little chimp had a kitten as a playmate and spent much time with it. She could not be fooled in the block game by instructions to point to the kitten if it were not visible. Although a familiar figure such as a chicken might be showing, Christine would not point to it or anything until she looked about her or turned over the blocks to reveal the kitten picture.

Christine viewed the quiz differently than her foster parent. The kitten was the name of the game as far as she was concerned. If Miss Hess set up the blocks showing both a chicken and kitten and asked for the chicken Christine seemed to hear only the first part of the question. Always she picked up the block with the kitten's picture. Miss Hess believed this was not the result of lack of understanding but a result of overwhelming affection for her kitten. Christine always made a fuss over the kitten block.

Can man converse with apes? Yes, it appears that people who have observed them sufficiently can understand the meaning of various sounds, gestures and expressions, and imitate them adequately to make themselves understood. A number of witnessed incidents corroborate this.

Learning ape sounds and meanings is no easy matter. Heinrich Oberjohann spent eight years in West African chimpanzee habitat before learning enough about chimpanzee sounds and gestures to understand and communicate with them. He found that simple chimpanzee sounds were included in various combinations in actual idioms as well as numerous mumbles, whines and mouthing sounds which expressed sentiments.

These sounds are not instinctive. Chimpanzee young have to learn the sounds from their mother and older associates. A chimpanzee separated early from its mother and reared in captivity cannot understand the language of other chimpanzees.

Julie Macdonald reared a young baboon (a monkey, not an ape) in her home. The baboon remained a baboon in most respects, rather than trying to imitate all human actions as the chimpanzee is apt to do. She studied her pet conscientiously and added significantly to the limited store of baboon literature. In her book *Almost Human* she compiled an appendix of baboon sounds and their meanings as well as the gestures which convey moods and sometimes surprising meanings. A baboon flicking its hands was in the second stage of threat, or belligerence.

George Schaller developed a list of twenty-two distinct gorilla vocalizations and their apparent meanings. He has identified sounds which are exclusive to male, female, juvenile and infant.

Memory in animals is often an indefinite thing, especially so when an attempt is made to correlate it with intellect. Elephants are supposed to have amazing memories, but about the only thing which elephants remember well in man's knowledge is a person who once caused them pain. Many animal species apparently remember such things all their lives.

Gerald Durrell took his chimpanzee called "Chum" to his native England and spent many pleasant hours traveling around the countryside on a motorcycle with a sidecar. Chum loved to ride in the sidecar and was well behaved except when passing other motorcycles. The chimpanzee loved to reach out and grab startled drivers.

On the first motorcycle ride, Durrell drove down to a garage for gasoline. Chum watched the garage man unscrew the filler cap and fill the tank. Two weeks later Durrell again stopped by for gasoline and was talking to the garage man briefly before gassing up. Puzzled at the man's stare past his shoulder, Durrell turned to see Chum trying to screw off the gas cap.

Chum was a keen observer, especially of details which interested him. During a long drive to London for a television show Chum sat on Durrell's lap while the latter's sister drove. They decided to stop at a pub and after passing several, Durrell picked one which seemed homely and quiet, one that would probably not bar the chimp. Fortunately, the pub owner was a lady who loved animals and she stuffed Chum with orange juice and potato chips. Chum had such a good time, including dancing on the bar, that he did not want to leave.

After three months Durrell had to go through the same area. Suddenly Chum began to jump up and down on Durrell's lap. Durrell thought that he was excited at seeing farm animals but there were none in sight. Chum grew more excited as they rounded a curve in the road.

Then Durrell saw the reason. The pub where Chum had enjoyed himself was directly ahead. They stopped and renewed acquaintances.

Strangely, ape intellect is a by-product of eye placement. Evolution put eyes in front of their heads instead of on the sides for a purpose. This placement gives them binocular, or three-dimensional, vision, a vital necessity for species which evolved in habitats requiring accurate leaps from limb to limb. The only primates not having true binocular vision are the primitive tree shrews.

Consequently, the dominant sense for primates is vision. A necessary foundation for the development and expansion of primate brains was a curious eye which motivated exploration. This was an essential ingredient in the development of man. The magnetism of curiosity and exploration brought man's ancestors out of the relative safety of trees into an open, insecure environment where brains meant survival.

Recently I examined basalt rock at the bottom of Tanzania's Olduvai Gorge which potassium-argon dating has fixed at almost 2,000,000 years old. This gorge has answered a horde of questions about man's kinship, or lack of it, to the apes. Two of the most important scientists of our time, Dr. Louis Leakey and his wife Mary, have spent most of their adult years sifting clues from this rich fossil region.

Mary Leakey found a skull of an early primate, *Zinjanthropus*, in 1959 whose age was fixed at 1,750,000 years. It was found among stone tools and at first was considered an intermediate species between man and ape, but sub-

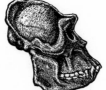

PROCONSUL   GORILLA   CHIMPANZEE

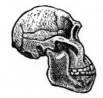

AUSTRALOPITHECUS   HOMO ERECTUS

NEANDERTHAL   CRO-MAGNON   MODERN MAN

sequent investigation indicates that it was one of the many blind alleys in the evolution of primates. It did not evolve into anything but became extinct.

A world-wide search has been underway at an increasing pace since Charles Darwin and Alfred Russell Wallace began one of the world's greatest debates by suggesting that today's species did not come to life suddenly in the year 4004 B. C. as Irish Archbishop James Ussher calculated, but developed instead as a result of orderly natural selection, i.e., evolution.

Darwin in his *Origin of the Species* said nothing about man's descent from anything, but some furious religious leaders and scientists felt that Darwin implied that man was descended from chimpanzees and gorillas. Now, education has largely erased these false notions of Darwin's theory of natural selection but unfortunate echoes can still be heard.

A year or so ago I sat in a church in one of our western states which prides itself on sophistication and modernity and heard a minister condemn with some vehemence both Dr. Leakey and Darwin. The false statements made by this minister seemed to be more the products of sheer ignorance than deliberate distortion. Such a man could never understand that the scientists who know most about the steps used by the Creator to produce today's world are more aware of God than those people whose ideas of creation were based on folktales evolved around the campfires of early mid-eastern sheepherders.

If man did not evolve from apes what did he evolve from? Present evidence indicates that his basic ancestor was a hominid, or man-like, primate called *Australopithecus*. This was essentially a pre-human but it had a short pelvis which showed that it walked erect, and had man's narrow face, arched forehead and rounded brain case. It lived from about 2,000,000 years to 1,000,000 years ago. It evolved into forms which included *Homo erectus* about 700,000 years ago, followed by the first *Homo sapiens*, then *Neanderthal* man about 100,000 years ago. All of modern man's races appear to have developed from *Cro-magnon* man which replaced *Neanderthal* man and spread over the world. Dr. Leakey believes that both *Zinjanthropus* and *Homo erectus* were dead ends in the evolutionary process.

Then what was the apes' ancestor? A creature called *Proconsul* lived roughly during the time span 22,000,000 to 12,000,000 years ago and is believed to be the ancestor of today's chimpanzees and gorillas. The stock that produced modern man may have broken away from *Proconsul* during this 10,000,000-year period.

Do apes and men have a common ancestor? No creature has been identified as such, although the search continues for every shred of evidence which will throw light on either's ancestry. Species which lived millions of years ago can leave many clues in their fossilized remains but at the moment no scientist can point to a fossil and say, "This creature was the common ancestor of man and ape." Dr. Leakey believes that we will never be able to designate a specific time and creature and identify it as man's beginning. Human development has been far too complex to allow such clear resolution.

Perhaps one of the most significant questions generated by man's increasing knowledge of life's beginnings and development is the probable content of the Book of Genesis had it been written today by an inspired scientist rather than an inspired chronicler of Israelite history.

Bibliography

Adamson, Joy. *Living Free.* Harcourt, Brace and World, Inc., 1961.

Akeley, Mary L. *Congo Eden.* Dodd Mead & Company, 1950.

Bevis, Margaret. *The Insects of Southern Africa.* Thomas Nelson and Sons (Africa) (PTY) Ltd., Johannesburg, 1964.

Burns, Eugene. *The Sex Life of Wild Animals.* Rinehart and Company, Inc., 1953.

Burroughs, Edgar Rice. *Tarzan of the Apes.* Frank A. Munsey Company, 1912.

Coughlan, Robert. *Tropical Africa.* Time, Inc., 1966.

Darwin, Charles. *The Origin of Species.* Washington Square Press, Inc., 1963.

Denis, Armand. *On Safari.* E. P. Dutton & Company, Inc., 1963.

Durrell, Gerald. *The Bafut Beagles.* Ballantine Books, Inc., 1966.

The Overloaded Ark. Ballantine Books, Inc., 1965.

A Zoo in My Luggage. Berkley Publishing Corporation, 1964.

Eimerl, Sarel and DeVore, Irven. *The Primates.* Time, Inc., 1965.

Elkington, B. D. and Guy, G. L. *The Bundu Book of Trees, Flowers and Grasses.* Longmans of Rhodesia (Pvt.) Ltd., 1965.

Feldman, Susan. *African Myths and Tales.* Dell Publishing Company, Inc., 1963.

Gatti, Attilio. *The King of the Gorillas.* Doubleday, Doran & Company, Inc., 1932.

Gourou, Pierre. *The Tropical World.* Longmans Green and Company, Ltd., London, 1958.

Grainger, Colonel D. H. *Don't Die in the Bundu.* Howard Timmins, Cape Town, 1967.

Gregory, William K. and Raven, Henry C. *In Quest of Gorillas.* The Darwin Press, 1937.

Hallet, Jean-Pierre. *Congo Kitabu.* Fawcett Publications, Inc., 1967.

Harlow, Harry F. "Of Love in Infants," *Natural History* magazine, May, 1960.

Harlow, Harry F. and Harlow, Margaret K. "A Study of Animal Affection," *Natural History* magazine, December, 1961.

Hediger, Dr. H. *Wild Animals in Captivity.* Dover Publications, Inc., 1964.

Hess, Lilo. "A Chimp in the Woods," *Natural History* magazine, March, 1957.

"Christine," Parts one and two, *Natural History* magazine, September, October, 1953.

Howell, F. Clark. *Early Man*. Time, Inc., 1965.

Johnson, Martin. *Congorilla*. Blue Ribbon Books Inc., 1931.

Lang, Ernst M. "Jambo, First Gorilla Raised in Captivity by its Mother," *National Geographic* magazine, March, 1964.

    Goma, The Baby Gorilla. Victor Gollancz, Ltd., London, 1962.

Leakey, Louis S. B. "Adventures in the Search for Man," *National Geographic* magazine, January, 1963.

    "Exploring 1,750,000 Years into Man's Past," *National Geographic* magazine, October, 1961.

Life Magazine Editors. "Private Life of Primates," LIFE magazine, February 19, 1965.

McDonald, Julie. *Almost Human*. Chilton Books, 1965.

Morris, Desmond. *The Biology of Art*. Alfred A. Knopf, 1962.

    The Naked Ape. McGraw Hill, 1967.

    "Primate's Aesthetics," *Natural History* magazine, January, 1961.

Morris, Ramona and Desmond. *Men and Apes*. McGraw-Hill, 1966.

Oberjohann, Heinrich. *My Best Friends Are Apes*. E. P. Dutton & Company, Inc., 1959.

Payne, Melvin M. "Family in Search of Prehistoric Man," *National Geographic* magazine, February, 1965.

    "Preserving the Treasures of Olduvai Gorge," *National Geographic* magazine, November, 1966.

Reynolds, Vernon. *Budongo*. The Natural History Press, 1965.

Riopelle, Arthur J. "Snowflake, The World's First White Gorilla," *National Geographic* magazine, March, 1967.

Sanderson, Ivan T. *The Monkey Kingdom.* Hanover House, 1957.

Sanderson, Ivan T. and Loth, David. *Ivan Sanderson's Book of Great Jungles.* Simon and Schuster, Inc., 1965.

Schaller, George B. *The Mountain Gorilla, Ecology and Behavior.* The University of Chicago Press, 1963.

> *The Year of the Gorilla.* The University of Chicago Press, 1964.

> "Mountain Gorilla Displays," *Natural History* magazine, August, 1963.

Scott, John Paul. *Animal Behavior.* Doubleday & Company, Inc., 1963.

Van Lawick-Goodall, Jane. *My Friends the Wild Chimpanzees.* National Geographic Society, 1967.

> "My Life Among Wild Chimpanzees," *National Geographic* magazine, August, 1963.

> "New Discoveries Among Africa's Chimpanzees," *National Geographic* magazine, December, 1965.

Wender, Leo. *Animal Encyclopedia.* George Allen and Unwin, Ltd., London, 1948.

Willock, Colin. *The Enormous Zoo.* Harcourt, Brace and World, Inc., 1965.

Zahl, Paul A. "Face to Face With Gorillas in Central Africa," *National Geographic* magazine, January, 1960.

Index

Tanzania, 15, 122
termite, 75–77
tick, 32
tiger, 101
Togoland, 35

Uganda, 8, 19, 22, 25
Uganda Game Department, 100
University of Wisconsin, 10
Ussher, Archbishop James, 124

van Lawick, Baron Hugo, 16, 79

Viki, 118
Virunga, 81

Wallace, Alfred Russell, 124
Washington, D.C., 14, 16
West Africa, 1, 25–29, 35, 48, 81, 82, 91, 100, 119
Wyman, 81

Yerkes, Robert, 9

Zinjanthropus, 122, 125